AS Maths

Edexcel Statistics 1

AS level maths is seriously tricky — no question about that.

We've done everything we can to make things easier for you.
We've scrutinised past paper questions and we've gone through the syllabuses with a fine-toothed comb. So we've found out exactly what you need to know, then explained it simply and clearly.

We've stuck in as many helpful hints as you could possibly want — then we even tried to put some funny bits in to keep you awake.

We've done our bit — the rest is up to you.

What CGP is all about

Our sole aim here at CGP is to produce the highest quality books — carefully written, immaculately presented and dangerously close to being funny.

Then we work our socks off to get them out to you — at the cheapest possible prices.

Contents

Section One — Data

Section Two — Probability

Section Three — Probability Distributions

Section Four — Correlation and Regression

In this book, all answers have been rounded off to an appropriate degree of accuracy (usually 3 significant figures).

This book covers the Statistics 1 module of the Edexcel specification

Published by CGP

Typesetters:
Martin Chester, Sharon Watson

Contributors:
Charley Darbishire, Dave Harding, Claire Jackson, Simon Little, Tim Major, Andy Park, Glenn Rogers, Garry Rowlands, Chris Worth

Updated by: Sam Norman, Ali Palin, Andy Park, Alan Rix, Glenn Rogers, Alice Shepperson, Claire Thompson, Sharon Watson

Many thanks to Vicky Daniel and Colin Wells *for proofreading.*

ISBN 978 1 84146 761 0

Based on the classic CGP style created by Richard Parsons.

Groovy website: www.cgpbooks.co.uk

Jolly bits of clipart from CorelDRAW®

Printed by Elanders Ltd, Newcastle upon Tyne.

Photocopying – it's dull, grey and sometimes a bit naughty. Luckily, it's dead cheap, easy and quick to order more copies of this book from CGP – just call us on 0870 750 1242. Phew!

Text, design, layout and original illustrations
© Coordination Group Publications Ltd. (CGP) 2004
All rights reserved.

Histograms

Histograms are glorified bar charts. The main difference is that you plot the frequency density (rather than the frequency). Frequency density is easy to find — you just divide the frequency by the width of a class.

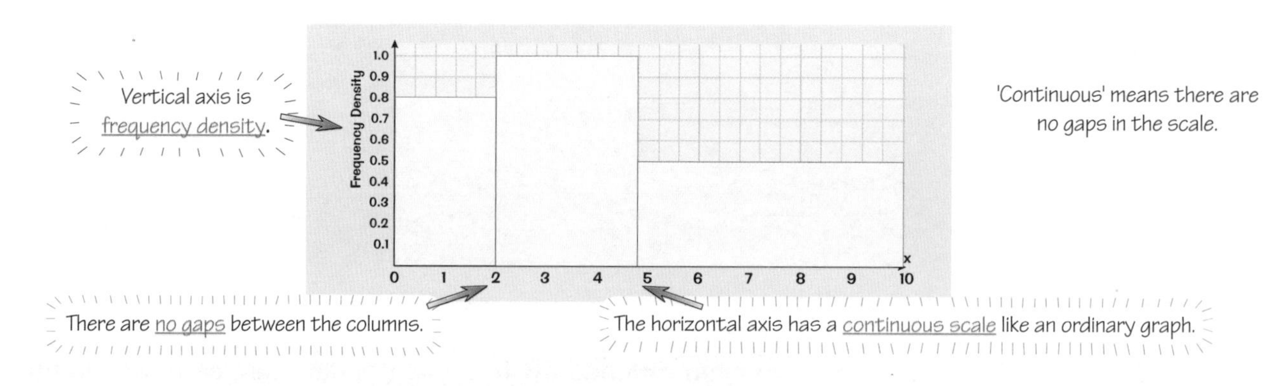

To Draw a **Histogram** it's best to Draw a **Table** First

Getting histograms right depends on finding the right upper and lower bounds for each class.

Example:

Draw a histogram to represent the data below showing the masses of parcels (given to the nearest 100 g).

Mass of parcel (to nearest 100 g)	100 - 200	300 - 400	500 - 700	800 - 1100
Number of parcels	100	250	600	50

First draw a table showing the upper and lower class bounds, plus the frequency density:

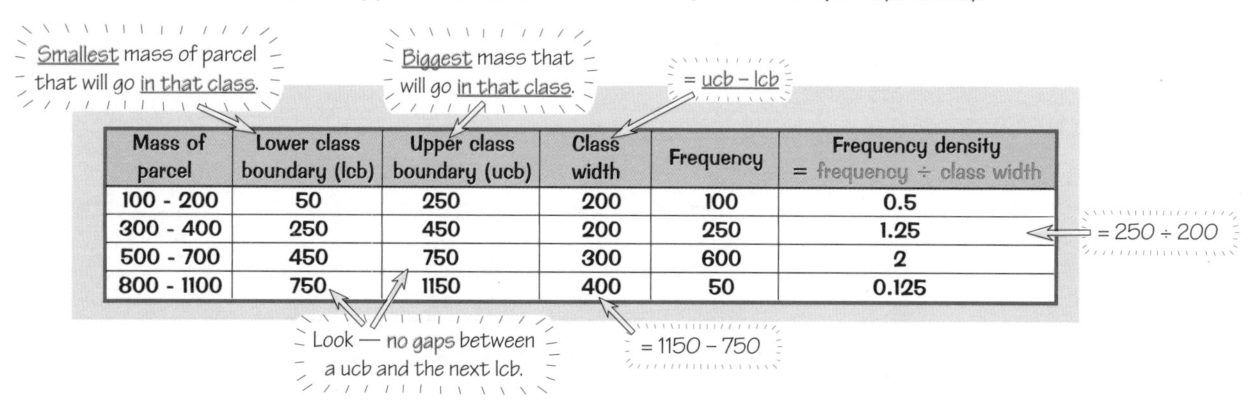

Mass of parcel	Lower class boundary (lcb)	Upper class boundary (ucb)	Class width	Frequency	Frequency density = frequency ÷ class width
100 - 200	50	250	200	100	0.5
300 - 400	250	450	200	250	1.25
500 - 700	450	750	300	600	2
800 - 1100	750	1150	400	50	0.125

Now you can draw the histogram.

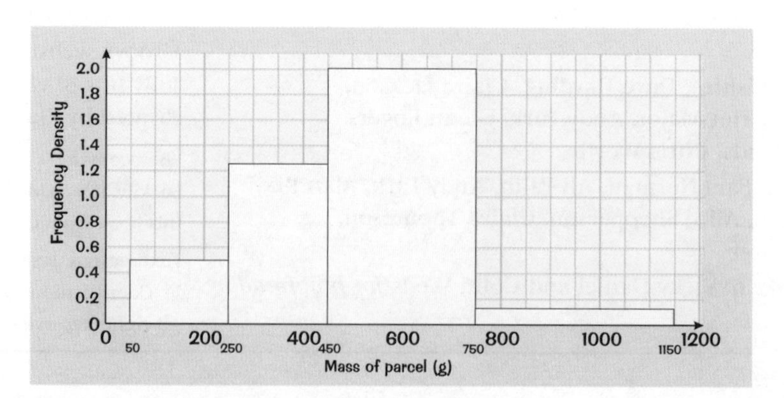

It's the area of each bar that shows the frequency — not the height.

Note: A class with a lower class boundary of 50 g and upper class boundary of 250 g can be written in different ways.
So you might see: "100 – 200 to nearest 100 g"
"50 ≤ mass < 250"
"50–", followed by "250–" for the next class and so on.
They all mean the same — just make sure you know how to spot the lower and upper class boundaries.

Stem and Leaf Diagrams

Stem and Leaf Diagrams look nothing like stems or leaves

They're just an easy way to represent your data. And they come in two flavours — plain or back-to-back.

Example: The lengths in metres of cars in a car park were measured to the nearest 10 cm.
Draw a stem and leaf diagram to show the following data: 2.9, 3.5, 4.0, 2.8, 4.1, 3.7, 3.1, 3.6, 3.8, 3.7

It's best to do a rough version first, and then put the 'leaves' in order afterwards.

My 'stems' are the numbers before the decimal point, and my 'leaves' are the numbers after.

It's a good idea to cross out the numbers (in pencil) as you add them to your diagram.

2	9, 8
3	5, 7, 1, 6, 8, 7
4	0, 1

Put the digits after the decimal point in order

2	8, 9
3	1, 5, 6, 7, 7, 8
4	0, 1

Key 2|9 means 2.9 m

Always give a key.

Digits after the decimal point — this row represents 4.0 m and 4.1 m.

Example: The heights of boys and girls in a year 11 class are given to the nearest cm in a back-to-back stem and leaf diagram below. Write out the data in full.

First boy, 8|16|, has height 168 cm. The boys are read backwards.

Key 8|16|5 means
Boys 168 cm and girls 165 cm

Boys		Girls
	15	9
8	16	1, 5, 9
9, 8, 1	17	0, 2, 3, 5
5, 2	18	0
1	19	

First girl, |15|9, has height 159 cm.

Boys: 168, 171, 178, 179, 182, 185, 191

Girls: 159, 161, 165, 169, 170, 172, 173, 175, 180

Practice Questions

1) *The stem and leaf diagram on the right represents the lengths (in cm) of 15 bananas. Write down the original data as a list.*

12	8
13	2, 5
14	3, 3, 6, 8
15	2, 9
16	1, 1, 2, 3
17	0, 2

Key 12|8 means 12.8 cm

2) *Construct a back-to-back stem and leaf diagram to represent the following data:*
Boys' test marks 34, 27, 15, 39, 20, 26, 32, 37, 19, 22
Girls' test marks 21, 38, 37, 12, 27, 28, 39, 29, 25, 24, 31, 36

3) *Twenty phone calls were made by a householder one evening. The lengths of the calls (in minutes to the nearest minute) are recorded below. Draw a histogram of the data.*

Length of call	0 - 2	3 - 5	6 - 8	9 - 15
Number of calls	10	6	3	1

Sample exam question:

4) The profits of 100 businesses are given in the table.

Profit, £x million.	Number of businesses
$4.5 \leqslant x < 5.0$	24
$5.0 \leqslant x < 5.5$	26
$5.5 \leqslant x < 6.0$	21
$6.0 \leqslant x < 6.5$	19
$6.5 \leqslant x < 8.0$	10

(a) Represent the data in a histogram. [3 marks]

(b) Comment on the distribution of the profits of the businesses. [2 marks]

First things first: remember — there are lies, damned lies and statistics...

Histograms shouldn't really cause too many problems — this is quite a friendly topic really. The main things to remember are to work out the lower and upper boundaries of each class properly, and then make sure you use frequency density (rather than just the frequency). Stem and leaf diagrams — hah, they're easy, I do them in my sleep. Make sure you can too.

Mean, Median, Mode and Range

The Definitions are really GCSE stuff

You more than likely already know them. But if you don't, learn them now — you'll be needing them loads.

Mean $= \bar{x} = \frac{\sum x}{n}$ or $\frac{\sum fx}{\sum f}$

The Σ (sigma) things just mean you add stuff up — so Σx means you add up all the values of x.

where each x is a data value, f is the frequency of each x (the number of times it occurs), and n is the total number of data values.

Median = middle data value when all the data values are placed in order of size.

Mode = most frequently occurring data value.

Range = highest value – lowest value

This will be the $\left(\frac{n+1}{2}\right)$th value in the ordered list.

Example: Find the mean, median, mode and range of the following list of data: 2, 3, 6, 2, 5, 9, 3, 8, 7, 2

Put in order first: 2, 2, 2, 3, 3, 5, 6, 7, 8, 9

Mean $= \frac{2+2+2+3+3+5+6+7+8+9}{10} = \underline{\mathbf{4.7}}$

Median = average of 5th and 6th values = average of 3 and 5 = **4**

Since $\frac{n+1}{2} = 5.5$

Mode = 2

Range = 9 – 2 = 7

Use a Table when there are a lot of Numbers

Example:

The number of letters received one day in 100 houses was recorded. Find the mean, median, mode and range of the number of letters.

Number of letters	Number of houses
0	11
1	25
2	27
3	21
4	9
5	7

The number of letters received by each house is a **discrete** quantity (e.g. 3 letters). There isn't a **continuous** set of possible values between getting 3 and 4 letters (e.g. 3.45 letters).

The first thing to do is make a table like this one:

Number of letters x	Number of houses f		fx
0	11	(11)	0
1	25	(36)	25
2	27	(63)	54
3	21		63
4	9		36
5	7		35
totals	100		213

Multiply x by f to get this column.

Put the running total in brackets — it's handy when you're finding the median. (But you can stop when you get past halfway.)

$\sum f = 100$

$\sum fx = 213$

① The mean is easy — just divide the total of the fx-column (sum of all the data values) by the total of the f-column (= n, the total number of data values).

Mean $= \frac{213}{100} =$ **2.13 letters**

② To find the position of the median, add 1 to the total frequency ($=\sum f = n$) and then divide by 2.
Here the median is in position: (100 + 1) ÷ 2 = 50.5.
So the median is halfway between the 50th and 51st data values.
Using your running total of f, you can see that the data values in positions 37 to 63 are all 2s. This means the data values at positions 50 and 51 are both 2 — so **Median = 2 letters**

③ The highest frequency is for 2 letters — so **Mode = 2 letters**

④ Range = highest data value – lowest data value. So **Range = 5 – 0 = 5 letters**

Mean, Median, Mode and Range

*If the data's **Grouped** you'll have to **Estimate***

If the data's grouped, you can only estimate the mean, median and mode.

There are no precise readings here — each reading's been put into one of these groups.

Example: The height of a number of trees was recorded. The data collected is shown in this table:

Height of tree to nearest m	0 - 5	6 - 10	11 - 15	16 - 20
Number of trees	26	17	11	6

Find an estimate of the mean height of the trees.

Here, you assume that every reading in that class takes the mid-class value (which you find by adding the lower class boundary to the upper class boundary and dividing by 2). It's best to make another table...

Height of tree to nearest m	mid-class value x	Number of trees f	fx
0 - 5	2.75	26 (26)	71.5
6 - 10	8	17 (43)	136
11 - 15	13	11	143
16 - 20	18	6	108
	Totals	60 (= Σf)	458.5(= Σfx)

Lower class boundary = 0.
Upper class boundary = 5.5.
So the mid-class value = (0 + 5.5) ÷ 2 = 2.75.

Estimated mean = $\frac{458.5}{60}$ = **7.64 m**

*Estimate the **Median** by assuming the values are **Evenly Spread***

The median position here is (60 + 1) ÷ 2 = 30.5, so the median is the 30.5th reading (halfway between the 30th and 31st). Your 'running total' tells you the median must be in the '6 - 10' class.
Now you have to assume that all the readings in this class are evenly spread.

There are 26 trees before class 6 - 10, so the 30.5th tree is the 4.5th value of this class.

Divide the class into 17 equally wide parts (as there are 17 readings) and assume there's a reading at the centre of each part.

Then you want the '4.5th reading' (which is '4 parts' along).

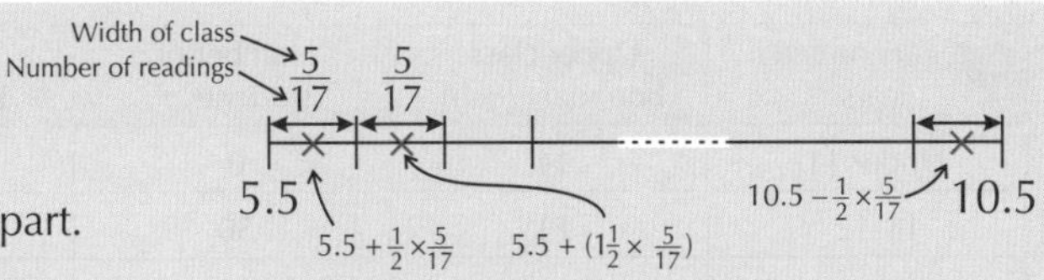

So the median = lower class boundary + (4 × width of each 'bit')

$$= 5.5 + \left[4 \times \frac{5}{17}\right] = 6.7\ m \text{ (to 1 d.p.)}$$

The **modal class** is the class with most readings in it. In this example the modal class is 0 - 5 m.

Practice Questions

1) *Calculate the mean, median and mode of the data in the table on the right.*

x	0	1	2	3	4
f	5	4	4	2	1

2) *The speeds of 60 cars travelling in a 40 mph speed limit area were measured to the nearest mph. The data is summarised in the table. Calculate estimates of the mean and median, and state the modal class.*

Speed (mph)	30 - 34	35 - 39	40 - 44	45 - 50
Frequency	12	37	9	2

Sample Exam Question:

3) The stem and leaf diagram shows the test marks for 30 male students and 16 female students.

(a) Find the median test mark of the male students. [1 mark]

(b) Compare the distribution of the male and female marks. [2 marks]

Male students		Female students
8, 3, 3	4	
8, 7, 7, 7, 5, 3, 2	5	5, 6, 7
9, 7, 6, 6, 5, 5, 2, 2, 1, 1, 0	6	1, 2, 3, 3, 4, 5, 6, 7, 9
9, 9, 8, 5, 4, 3, 1, 0, 0	7	2, 4, 8, 9

Key 5|6|2 means Male student test mark 65 and Female student test mark 62

I can't deny it — this page really is kind of average...

Doing all this stuff isn't that hard — it's remembering all the different names that gives me a headache. But it's all made easier if you learn that the MeDian is the one in the MiDdle, while the MOde is the one that there's MOst of. The mean, well, that's just your common or garden 'average' that you learnt about while you were still in short trousers.

Cumulative Frequency Diagrams

Quartiles divide the data into Four

The median divides the data into two — the quartiles divide the data into four.

Example: Find the median and quartiles of the following data: 2, 5, 3, 11, 6, 7, 1

First put the list in order: 1 2 3 5 6 7 11

There are 7 numbers, so the median is in position 4 (i.e. you take the fourth number along): Median = 5

The middle of the set of numbers below the median is the lower quartile (Q_1) and the middle of the set above the median is the upper quartile (Q_3). ⟹ 1 2 3 5 6 7 11 (Q_1 = 2, Q_3 = 7)

About 25% of the readings are less than the lower quartile. About 75% are less than the upper quartile.

Lower quartile = 2 Upper quartile = 7

Use Cumulative Frequency Graphs to find the Median and Quartiles

Cumulative frequency means 'running total'. Cumulative frequency diagrams make medians and quartiles easy to find...

Example: The ages of 200 students in a school are recorded in the table below.

Draw a cumulative frequency graph and use it to estimate the median age and the interquartile range.
Also estimate how many students are older than 18.

Age in completed years	11 - 12	13 - 14	15 - 16	17 - 18
Number of students	50	65	58	27

① First draw a table showing the upper class boundaries and the cumulative frequency:

Age in completed years	Upper class boundary (ucb)	Number of students, f	Cumulative frequency (cf)
Under 11	11	0	0
11-12	13	50	50
13-14	15	65	115
15-16	17	58	173
17-18	19	27	200

The first reading in a cumulative frequency table must be zero — so add this extra row to show the number of students with age less than 11 is 0.

CF is the number of students with age less than the ucb — it's the same thing as your running total from the last two pages.

The last number in the CF column should always be the total number of readings.

People say they're '18' right up until their 19th birthday — so the ucb of class 17-18 is 19.

Next draw the axes — cumulative frequency always goes on the vertical axis. Here, age goes on the other axis.
Then plot the upper class boundaries against the cumulative frequencies, and join the points.

② To find the median from a graph, go to the median position on the vertical scale and read off the value from the horizontal axis.

Median position = $\frac{1}{2}(200+1)=100.5$ so Median = 14.5 years

Then you can find the **quartiles** in the same way. Find their positions first:

Q_1 position = $\frac{1}{4}\times(200+1)=50.25$ (i.e. between the 50th and 51st readings)

Q_3 position = $\frac{3}{4}\times(200+1)=150.75$ (between the 150th and 151st readings)

Lower quartile, Q_1 = 13 years Upper quartile, Q_3 = 16.2 years

The **interquartile range** (IQR) = $Q_3 - Q_1$. It measures spread.
The smaller it is the less spread the data is.

IQR = $Q_3 - Q_1$ = 16.2 – 13 = 3.2 years

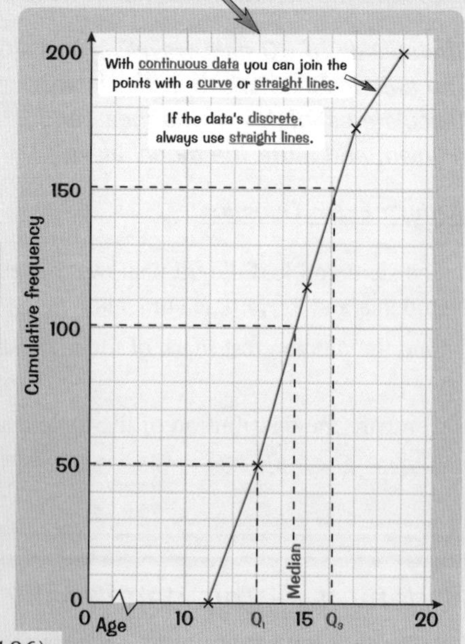

Always plot the upper class boundary of each class.

③ To find how many students are older than 18, first go up from 18 on the horizontal axis, and read off the number of students younger than 18 (= 186).

Then the number of students older than 18 is just 200 – 186 = 14 (approximately)

Cumulative Frequency Diagrams

Percentiles divide the data into 100

Percentiles divide the data into 100 — the median is the 50th percentile and Q_1 is the 25th percentile, etc.

Example:

The position of the 11th percentile (P_{11}) is $\frac{11}{100} \times$ (total frequency +1) $= \frac{11}{100} \times 201 = 22.11$

Or by going $\frac{11}{100}$ up the graph, you can see the 11th percentile is about 12.

You find interpercentile ranges by subtracting two percentiles, e.g. the middle 60% of the readings = $P_{80} - P_{20}$.

Box and Whisker Diagrams are useful for comparing distributions

Box and whisker plots show the median and quartiles in an easy-to-look-at kind of way...
These are sometimes called box plots.

They look like this:

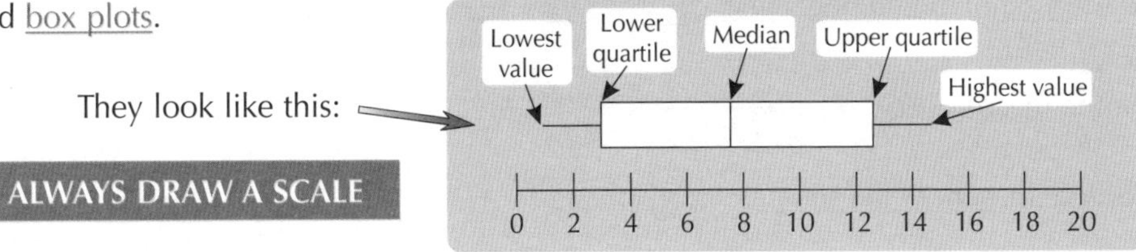

ALWAYS DRAW A SCALE

Practice Questions

1) ***Draw a cumulative frequency diagram of the data given in the table. Use your diagram to estimate the median and interquartile range.***

Distance walked (km)	0 - 2	2 - 4	4 - 6	6 - 8
Number of walkers	10	5	3	2

Sample Exam questions:

2) A shopkeeper records the age of the customers that enter his shop before 9:00 am one morning.

Age of customer in completed years	5 - 10	11 - 15	16 - 20	21 - 30	31 - 40	41 - 70
Number of customers	2	3	10	2	2	1

(a) On graph paper, draw a cumulative frequency diagram. [4 marks]

(b) From your graph estimate

(i) the median age of the customers. [1 mark]

(ii) the number of customers at least 12 years old. [2 marks]

3) Two workers iron clothes. Each irons 10 items, and records the time it takes them for each, to the nearest minute.

Worker A: 3 5 2 7 10 4 5 5 4 12

Worker B: 3 4 8 6 7 8 9 10 11 9

(a) For worker A's times. Find:

(i) the median, [1 mark]

(ii) the lower and upper quartiles. [2 marks]

(b) On graph paper draw, using the same scale, two box plots to represent the times of each worker. [6 marks]

(c) Make one statement comparing the two sets of data. [1 mark]

(d) Which worker would be best to employ? Give a reason for you answer. [1 mark]

WG Grace — an old-time box and whisker man...

Cumulative frequency sounds a bit scarier than running total — but if you remember that they're the same thing, that'll help. You might get a question on quartiles... to find these, you have to find the median of the bottom half and the median of the top half of the data — not including the middle value in either half if you have an odd number of values.

Variance and Standard Deviation

Standard deviation and variance both measure how spread out the data is from the mean — the bigger the variance, the more spread out your readings are.

The **Formulas** look pretty **Tricky**

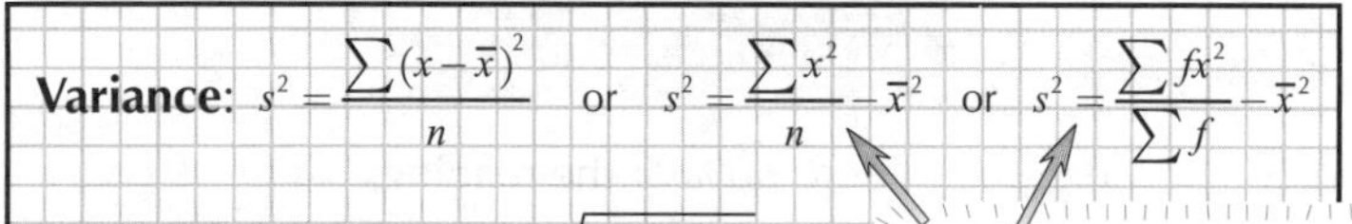

Variance: $s^2 = \frac{\sum(x-\bar{x})^2}{n}$ or $s^2 = \frac{\sum x^2}{n} - \bar{x}^2$ or $s^2 = \frac{\sum fx^2}{\sum f} - \bar{x}^2$

Standard deviation: $s = \sqrt{\text{variance}}$

The formula is easier to use in this form.

The x-values are the data, $\bar{x}$ is the mean, f is the frequency of each x and n is the number of data values.

Example: Find the mean and standard deviation of the following numbers: 2, 3, 4, 4, 6, 11, 12

1) Find the total of the numbers first: $\sum x = 2+3+4+4+6+11+12 = 42$
2) Then the mean is easy: $\text{Mean} = \bar{x} = \frac{\sum x}{n} = \frac{42}{7} = 6$
3) Next find the sum of the squares: $\sum x^2 = 4+9+16+16+36+121+144 = 346$
4) Use this to find the variance: $\text{Variance, } s^2 = \frac{\sum x^2}{n} - \bar{x}^2 = \frac{346}{7} - 6^2 = 49.43 - 36 = 13.43$
5) And take the square root to find the standard deviation: $\text{Standard deviation} = \sqrt{13.43} = 3.66$ to 3 sig. fig.

Questions about **Standard Deviation** can look a bit **Weird**

They can ask questions about standard deviation in different ways. But you just need to use the same old formulas.

Example:

The mean of 10 boys' heights is 180 cm, and the standard deviation is 10 cm. The mean for 9 girls is 165 cm, and the standard deviation is 8 cm. Find the mean and standard deviation of the whole group of 19 girls and boys.

(1) Let the boys' heights be x and the girls' heights be y.

Write down the formula for the mean and put the numbers in for the boys: $\bar{x} = \frac{\sum x}{n} \Rightarrow 180 = \frac{\sum x}{10} \Rightarrow \sum x = 1800$

Do the same for the girls: $165 = \frac{\sum y}{9} \Rightarrow \sum y = 1485$

So the sum of the heights for the boys and the girls = $\sum x + \sum y = 1800 + 1485 = 3285$

And the mean height of the boys and the girls is: $\frac{3285}{19} = 172.9$ cm

Round the fraction to 1 dp to give your answer. But if you need to use the mean in more calculations, use the fraction (or your calculator's memory) so you don't lose accuracy.

(2) Now for the variance — write down the formula for the boys first: $s_x^2 = \frac{\sum x^2}{n} - \bar{x}^2 \Rightarrow 10^2 = \frac{\sum x^2}{10} - 180^2 \Rightarrow \sum x^2 = 10\times(100+32400) = 325000$

Do the same for the girls: $s_y^2 = \frac{\sum y^2}{n} - \bar{y}^2 \Rightarrow 8^2 = \frac{\sum y^2}{9} - 165^2 \Rightarrow \sum y^2 = 9\times(64+27225) = 245601$

Okay, so the sum of the squares of the heights of the boys and the girls is: $\sum x^2 + \sum y^2 = 325000 + 245601 = 570601$

Which means the variance of all the heights is: $s^2 = \frac{570601}{19} - \left(\frac{3285}{19}\right)^2 = 139.0 \text{ cm}^2$

Don't use the rounded mean (172.9) — you'll lose accuracy.

And finally the standard deviation of the boys and the girls is: $s = \sqrt{139.0} = 11.8$ cm

Phew.

Variance and Standard Deviation

Use Mid-Class Values if your data's in a Table

With grouped data, assume every reading takes the mid-class value. Then use the frequencies to find $\sum fx$ and $\sum fx^2$.

Example: The heights of sunflowers in a garden were measured and recorded in the table below. Estimate the mean height and the standard deviation.

Height of sunflower	$150 \le x < 170$	$170 \le x < 190$	$190 \le x < 210$	$210 \le x < 230$
Number of sunflowers	5	10	12	3

Draw up another table, and include columns for the mid-class values x, as well as fx and fx^2:

Height of sunflower	Mid-class value, x	x^2	f	fx	fx^2
$150 \le x < 170$	160	25600	5	800	128000
$170 \le x < 190$	180	32400	10	1800	324000
$190 \le x < 210$	200	40000	12	2400	480000
$210 \le x < 230$	220	48400	3	660	145200
		Totals	30 $(= \Sigma f)$	5660 $(= \Sigma fx)$	1077200 $(= \Sigma fx^2)$

fx^2 means $f \times (x^2)$ — not $(fx)^2$.

Now you've got the totals in the table, you can calculate the mean and variance:

$$\text{Mean} = \bar{x} = \frac{\sum fx}{\sum f} = \frac{5660}{30} = 189 \text{ to 3 sig. fig.}$$

$$\text{Variance} = s^2 = \frac{\sum fx^2}{\sum f} - \bar{x}^2 = \frac{1077200}{30} - \bar{x}^2 = 312 \text{ to 3 sig. fig.}$$

$$\text{Standard deviation} = \sqrt{312} = 17.7 \text{ to 3 sig. fig.}$$

Practice Questions

1) ***Find the mean and standard deviation of the following numbers: 11, 12, 14, 17, 21, 23, 27.***

2) ***The scores in an IQ test for 50 people are recorded in the table below.***

Score	100 - 106	107 - 113	114 - 120	121 - 127	128 - 134
Frequency	6	11	22	9	2

Calculate the mean and variance of the distribution.

Sample Exam question:

3) In a supermarket two types of chocolate drops were compared.
The weights (in grams) of 20 chocolate drops of brand A are summarised by:

$$\sum A = 60.3 \text{ g} \qquad \sum A^2 = 219 \text{ g}^2$$

The mean weight of 30 chocolate drops of brand B was 2.95 g, and the standard deviation was 1 g.

(a) Find the mean weight of a brand A chocolate drop. [1 mark]

(b) Find the standard deviation of the weight of the brand A chocolate drops. [3 marks]

(c) Compare brands A and B. [2 marks]

(d) Find the standard deviation of the weight of all 50 chocolate drops. [4 marks]

People who enjoy this stuff are standard deviants...

The formula for the variance looks pretty scary, what with the s's and $\bar{x}$'s floating about. But it comes down to 'the mean of the squares minus the square of the mean'. That's how I remember it anyway — and my memory's rubbish.
Ooh, while I remember... don't forget to work out mid-class values carefully, using the upper and lower class boundaries.

Coding

Coding means doing something to every reading (like adding a number, or multiplying by a number) to make life easier.

Coding can make the Numbers much Easier

Finding the mean of 1001, 1002 and 1006 looks hard(ish). But take 1000 off each number and finding the mean of what's left (1, 2 and 6) is much easier — it's 3. So the mean of the original numbers must be 1003. That's coding.

You usually change your original variable x to an easier one to work with y (so here, if $x = 1001$, then $y = 1$).

Write down a formula connecting the two variables: e.g. $y = \frac{x-b}{a}$.

You can add/subtract a number, and multiply/divide by one as well — it all depends on what will make life easiest.

Then $\bar{y} = \frac{\bar{x}-b}{a}$ where $\bar{x}$ and $\bar{y}$ are the means of variables x and y.

Also $s_y = \frac{s_x}{a}$ where s_x and s_y are the standard deviations of variables x and y.

Note that if you don't multiply or divide your readings by anything (i.e. if a = 1), then the spread isn't changed.

Example: Find the mean and standard deviation of: 1 000 020, 1 000 040, 1 000 010 and 1 000 050.

The obvious thing to do is subtract a million from every reading to leave 20, 40, 10 and 50.
Then make life even simpler by dividing by 10 — giving 2, 4, 1 and 5.

1. So use the coding: $y = \frac{x-1000000}{10}$. Then $\bar{y} = \frac{\bar{x}-1000000}{10}$ and $s_y = \frac{s_x}{10}$.

2. Find the mean and standard deviation of the y values: $\bar{y} = \frac{2+4+1+5}{4} = 3$ $\quad s_y = \sqrt{\frac{2^2+4^2+1^2+5^2}{4} - 3^2} = \sqrt{\frac{46}{4} - 9} = \sqrt{2.5}$ $= 1.58$ to 3 sig. fig.

3. Then use the formulas to find the mean and standard deviation of the original values:

$\bar{x} = 10\bar{y} + 1000000 = (10 \times 3) + 1000000 = 1000030$ $\qquad s_x = 10 s_y = 10 \times 1.58 = 15.8$

You can use coding with Summarised Data

This kind of question looks tricky at first — but use the same old formulas and it's a piece of cake.

Example: A set of 10 numbers (x-values) can be summarised as shown: $\sum(x-10) = 15$ and $\sum(x-10)^2 = 100$
Find the mean and standard deviation of the numbers.

1. Okay, the obvious first thing to try is: $y = x - 10$

   That means: $\sum y = 15$ and $\sum y^2 = 100$

2. Work out $\bar{y}$ and s_y^2 using the normal formulas: $\bar{y} = \frac{\sum y}{n} = \frac{15}{10} = 1.5$

   $s_y^2 = \frac{\sum y^2}{n} - \bar{y}^2 = \frac{100}{10} - 1.5^2 = 10 - 2.25 = 7.75$

   so $s_y = 2.78$ to 3 sig. fig.

3. Then finding the mean and standard deviation of the x-values is easy: $\bar{x} = \bar{y} + 10 = 1.5 + 10 = 11.5$

   The spread of x is the same as the spread of y since you've only subtracted 10 from every number. $s_x = s_y = 2.78$ to 3 sig. fig.

Coding

Sensible Coding can make life Much Easier

Find the mean and standard deviation of the data in this table:

Class	10 - 19	20 - 29	30 - 39
f	2	5	3

It's grouped data, so use mid-class values — these are x = 14.5, 24.5 and 34.5.

Now let $y = \frac{x - 24.5}{10}$ and then draw up another table: This coding will make all the numbers in the table dead easy.

Class	Mid-class x	$y = \frac{x-24.5}{10}$	f	fy	fy^2
10 - 19	14.5	-1	2	-2	2
20 - 29	24.5	0	5	0	0
30 - 39	34.5	1	3	3	3
		Totals	10 (= Σf)	1 (= Σfy)	5 (= Σfy^2)

$\bar{y} = \frac{\sum fy}{\sum f} = \frac{1}{10} = 0.1$ and $s_y^2 = \frac{\sum fy^2}{10} - \bar{y}^2 = \frac{5}{10} - 0.1^2 = 0.5 - 0.01 = 0.49$

So $s_y = 0.7$

But $y = \frac{x - 24.5}{10}$ so $\bar{y} = \frac{\bar{x} - 24.5}{10}$, which means $\bar{x} = 10\bar{y} + 24.5 = (10 \times 0.1) + 24.5 = 25.5$

Since everything has been divided by 10, the spread of y is not the same as the spread of x.

In fact, $s_y = \frac{s_x}{10}$ so $s_x = 10 s_y = 7$

Practice Questions

**1) For a set of data, $n = 100$, $\sum(x - 20) = 125$, and $\sum(x - 20)^2 = 221$.
Find the mean and standard deviation of x.**

2) The time taken (to the nearest minute) for a commuter to travel to work on 20 consecutive days is recorded in the table. Use coding to find the mean and standard deviation of the times.

Time to nearest minute	30 - 33	34 - 37	38 - 41	42 - 45
Frequency	3	6	7	4

Sample Exam question:

3) A group of 19 people played a game. The scores, x, that the people achieved are summarised by:

$$\sum(x-30) = 228 \text{ and } \sum(x-30)^2 = 3040$$

(a) Calculate the mean and the standard deviation of the 19 scores. [3 marks]

(b) Show that $\sum x = 798$ and $\sum x^2 = 33820$. [3 marks]

(c) Another student played the game. Her score was 32.
Find the new mean and standard deviation of all 20 scores. [4 marks]

I thought the coding page would be a little more... well, James Bond...

Coding data isn't hard — the only tricky thing can be to work out how best to code it, although there will usually be some pretty hefty clues in the question if you care to look. But remember that adding/subtracting a number from every reading won't change the spread (the variance or standard deviation), but multiplying/dividing readings by something will.

Skewness and Outliers

Skewness tells you whether your data is symmetrical — or kind of lopsided.

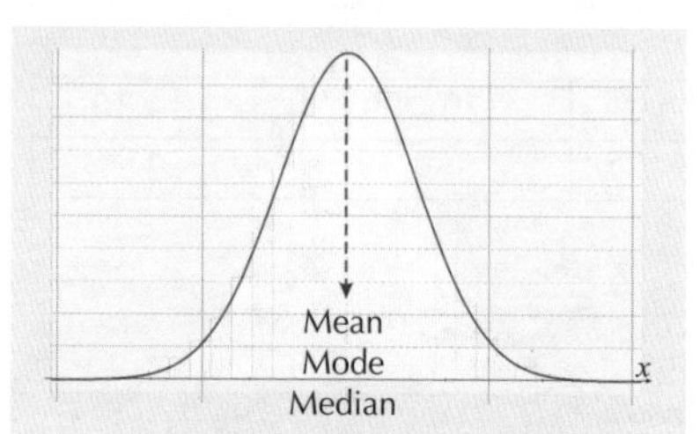

This is a typical symmetrical distribution.

Notice: mean = median = mode

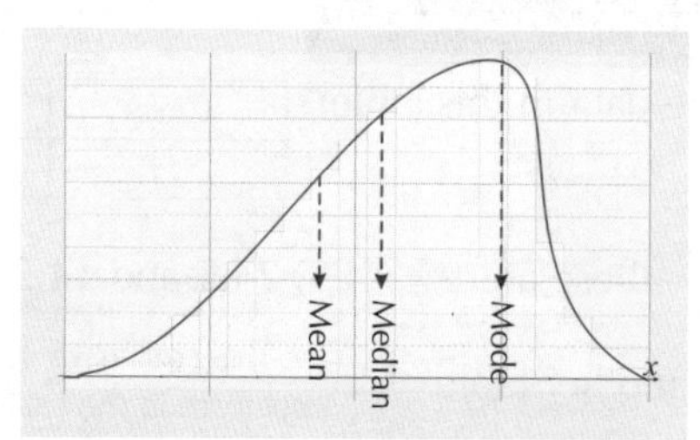

A negatively skewed distribution has a tail on the left. Most data values are on the higher side.

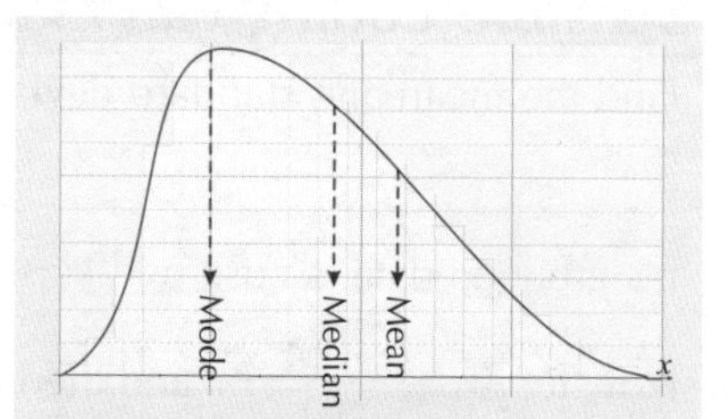

A positively skewed distribution has a tail on the right. Most data values are on the lower side.

For all distributions: **mean – mode = 3 × (mean – median)** — approximately.

Measure skewness using ***Pearson's Coefficient of Skewness...***

A coefficient of skewness measures how 'all-up-one-end' your data is. You need to know a couple of formulas...

$$\text{Pearson's coefficient of skewness} = \frac{\text{mean} - \text{mode}}{\text{standard deviation}} = \frac{3(\text{mean} - \text{median})}{\text{standard deviation}}$$

This usually lies between -3 and +3.
So if Pearson's coefficient of skewness is -0.1, then the distribution is slightly negatively skewed.

...or the ***Quartile Coefficient of Skewness***

Remember that Q_1 is the lower quartile, Q_3 is the upper quartile, and the median is Q_2.

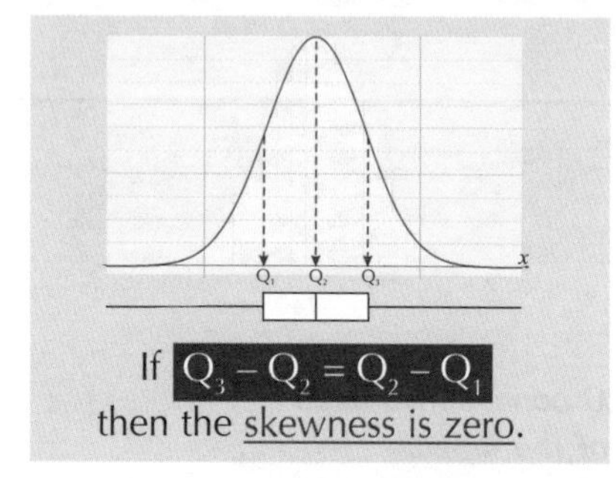

If $Q_3 - Q_2 = Q_2 - Q_1$ then the skewness is zero.

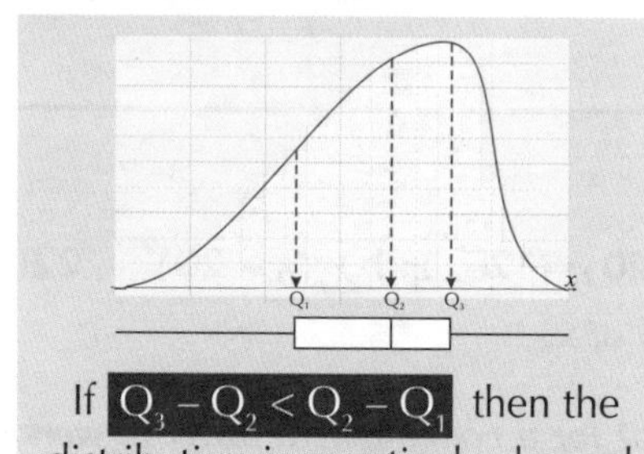

If $Q_3 - Q_2 < Q_2 - Q_1$ then the distribution is negatively skewed.

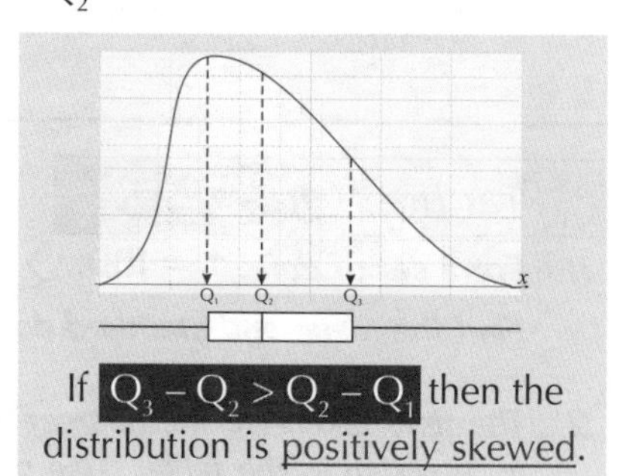

If $Q_3 - Q_2 > Q_2 - Q_1$ then the distribution is positively skewed.

$$\text{Quartile coefficient of skewness} = \frac{(Q_3 - Q_2) - (Q_2 - Q_1)}{Q_3 - Q_1} = \frac{Q_3 - 2Q_2 + Q_1}{Q_3 - Q_1}$$

Example: This table summarises the marks obtained in Maths 'calculator' and 'non-calculator' papers.

Calculate the Pearson's and Quartile coefficients of skewness for each paper. Comment on the distributions.

Calculator Paper		Non-calculator paper
40	Lower quartile, Q_1	35
58	Median, Q_2	42
70	Upper quartile, Q_3	56
55	Mean	46.1
21.2	Standard deviation	17.8

The quartile coefficient of skewness tells you that the calculator paper scores are slightly negatively skewed and that the non-calculator paper scores are positively skewed.

Calculator Paper		Non-calculator Paper
$\frac{3\times(55.0-58)}{21.2} = \frac{-9}{21.2} = -0.425$	Pearson's coefficient of skewness	$\frac{3\times(46.1-42)}{17.8} = \frac{12.3}{17.8} = 0.691$
$\frac{70-2\times58+40}{70-40} = \frac{-6}{30} = -0.2$	Quartile coefficient of skewness	$\frac{56-2\times42+35}{56-35} = \frac{7}{21} = 0.333$

Generally students have done better (compared to the mean) on the calculator paper.
Pearson's coefficient of skewness confirms these results.

Skewness and Outliers

An outlier is a freak piece of data that lies a long way from the rest of the readings.
To find whether a reading is an outlier you have to measure how far away from the rest of the data it is.

Outliers fall Outside Fences

There are various ways to decide if a reading is an outlier — the method you should use is always described in the question.

Example: A data value is considered to be an outlier if it is more than 3 times the IQR above the upper quartile or more than 3 times the IQR below the lower quartile.

The lower and upper quartiles of a data set are 70 and 100. Decide whether the data values 20 and 210 are outliers.

First you need the IQR: $Q_3 - Q_1 = 100 - 70 = 30$

Then it's a piece of cake to find where your fences are.

Lower fence first: $Q_1 - (3 \times \text{IQR}) = 70 - (3 \times 30) = -20$

And the upper fence: $Q_3 + (3 \times \text{IQR}) = 100 + (3 \times 30) = 190$

-20 and 190 are called fences. Any reading lying outside the fences is considered an outlier.

20 is inside the lower fence, so it is not an outlier. 210 is outside the upper fence, so it is an outlier.

Practice Questions

1) ***A data value is considered an outlier if it's more than 3 times the IQR above the upper quartile or more than 3 times the IQR below the lower quartile.***
If the lower and upper quartiles of a data set are 62 and 88, decide which of the following data are outliers:
a) 161, b) 176, c) 0

2) ***Find the median and quartiles of the data below. Draw a box and whisker diagram, and comment on any skewness.***
Amount of pocket money (in £) received per week by twenty 15-year-olds:
10, 5, 20, 50, 5, 1, 6, 5, 15, 20, 5, 7, 5, 10, 12, 4, 8, 6, 7, 30.

3) ***A set of data has a mean of 10.3, a mode of 10 and a standard deviation of 1.5.***
Calculate Pearson's coefficient of skewness, and draw a possible sketch of the distribution.

Practice Exam Questions:

4) The table shows the number of hits received at a paint ball party.

No. of Hits	12	13	14	15	16	17	18	19	20	21	22	23	24	25
Frequency	2	4	6	7	6	4	4	2	1	1	0	0	0	1

(a) Find the median and mode number of hits. [3 marks]

(b) An outlier is a data value which is greater than $3(Q_3 - Q_1)$ above Q_3 or below Q_1.
Is 25 an outlier? Show your working. [2 marks]

(c) Sketch a box plot of the distribution and comment on any skewness. [2 marks]

(d) How would the shape of the distribution be affected if the value of 25 was removed? [1 mark]

5) The data in the table shows the number of mm of rain that fell on 30 days on a tropical island.

mm of rain	5 - 10	10 - 15	15 - 20	20 - 25	25 - 30	30 - 35
No. of days	2	3	5	7	10	3

(a) Draw a cumulative frequency diagram of the data. [3 marks]

(b) Using your diagram estimate the median and quartiles. [3 marks]

(c) Calculate the quartile coefficient of skewness and describe the shape. [2 marks]

'Outlier' is the name I give to something that my theory can't explain...

Those definitions of positive and negative skew aren't the most obvious in the world — and it's easy to get them mixed up. Remember that negative skew involves a tail on the left, which means that a lot of your readings are on the high side. Positive skew is the opposite — a tail on the right, and a bunch of readings that are a little on the low side.

Random Events and Their Probability

Random events happen by chance. Probability is a measure of how likely they are. It can be a chancy business.

A Random Event has Various Outcomes

1) In a trial (or experiment) the things that can happen are called outcomes (so if I time how long it takes to eat my dinner, 63 seconds is a possible outcome).
2) Events are 'groups' of one or more outcomes (so an event might be 'it takes me less than a minute to eat my dinner every day one week').
3) When all outcomes are equally likely, you can work out the probability of an event by counting the outcomes.

$$\text{P(event)} = \frac{\text{Number of outcomes where event happens}}{\text{Total number of possible outcomes}}$$

Example: Suppose I've got a bag with 15 balls in — 5 red, 6 blue and 4 yellow.

If I take a ball out without looking, then any ball is equally likely — there are 15 possible outcomes. Of these 15 outcomes, 5 are red, 6 are blue and 4 are yellow. And so...

$\text{P(red ball)} = \frac{5}{15} = \frac{1}{3}$ $\text{P(blue ball)} = \frac{6}{15} = \frac{2}{5}$ $\text{P(yellow ball)} = \frac{4}{15}$

You can find the probability of either a red or a yellow ball in a similar way...

$\text{P(red or yellow ball)} = \frac{9}{15} = \frac{3}{5}$

The Sample Space is the Set of All Possible Outcomes

Drawing the sample space (called S) helps you count the outcomes you're interested in.

Example: The classic probability machine is a dice. If you roll it twice, you can record all the possible outcomes in a 6 × 6 table (a possible diagram of the sample space).

There are 36 outcomes in total. You can find probabilities by counting the ones you're interested in (and using the above formula). For example:

(i) The probability of an odd number and then a '1'. There are 3 outcomes that make up this event, so the probability is: $\frac{3}{36} = \frac{1}{12}$

(ii) The probability of the total being 7. There are 6 outcomes that correspond to this event, giving a probability of: $\frac{6}{36} = \frac{1}{6}$

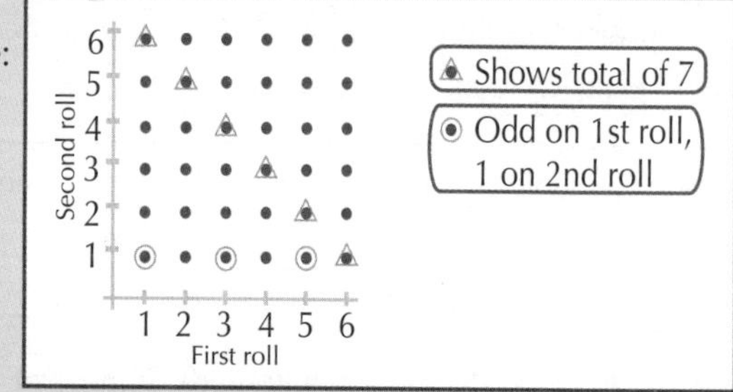

Venn Diagrams show which Outcomes correspond to which Events

Say you've got 2 events, A and B — a Venn diagram shows which outcomes satisfy event A, which satisfy B, which satisfy both, and which satisfy neither.

(i) All outcomes satisfying event A go in one part of the diagram, and all outcomes satisfying event B go in another bit.

(ii) If they satisfy 'both A and B', they go in the dark green middle bit, written $A \cap B$ (and called the intersection of A and B).

(iii) The whole of the green area is written $A \cup B$ — it means 'either A or B' (and is called the union of A and B).

Again, you can work out probabilities of events by counting outcomes and using the formula above.

You can also get a nice formula linking $P(A \cap B)$ and $P(A \cup B)$.

$$P(A \cup B) = P(A) + P(B) - P(A \cap B)$$

If you just add up the outcomes in A and B, you end up counting $A \cap B$ twice — that's why you have to subtract it.

Example: If you roll a dice, event A could be 'I get an even number', and B 'I get a number bigger than 4'. The Venn diagram would be:

$P(A) = \frac{3}{6} = \frac{1}{2}$ $P(B) = \frac{2}{6} = \frac{1}{3}$ $P(A \cap B) = \frac{1}{6}$ $P(A \cup B) = \frac{4}{6} = \frac{2}{3}$

Here, I've just counted outcomes — but I could have used the formula.

Random Events and Their Probability

Venn Diagrams make it easy to get your head round Tricky Things

Example: A survey was carried out to find what pets people like.

The probability they like dogs is 0.6. The probability they like cats is 0.5. The probability they like gerbils is 0.4. The probability they like dogs and cats is 0.4. The probability they like cats and gerbils is 0.1, and the probability they like gerbils and dogs is 0.2. Finally, the probability they like all three kinds of animal is 0.1.

You can draw all this in a Venn diagram. (Here I've used C for 'likes cats', D for 'likes dogs' and G for 'likes gerbils'.)

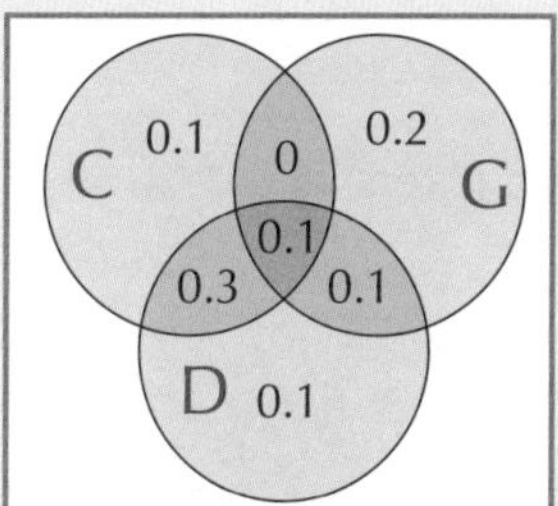

1) Stick in the middle one first — 'likes all 3 animals' (i.e. $C \cap D \cap G$).
2) Then do the 'likes 2 animals' probabilities by taking 0.1 from each of the given 'likes 2 animals' probabilities. (If they like 3 animals, they'll also be in the 'likes 2 animals' bits.)
3) Finally, do the 'likes 1 kind of animal' probabilities, by making sure the total probability in each circle adds up to the probability in the question.

① From the Venn diagram, the probability that someone likes either dogs or cats is 0.7.

② The probability that someone likes gerbils but not dogs is 0.2.

③ The probability that someone likes cats or dogs, but not gerbils is 0.5.

Practice Questions

1. A dice and a coin are thrown and the outcomes recorded.
If a head is thrown, the score on the dice is doubled. If a tail is thrown, 4 is added to the score on the dice.
- ***a) Represent this by means of a sample space diagram.***
- ***b) What is the probability that you score more than 5?***
- ***c) If you throw a tail, what is the probability that you get an even score?***

2. Half the students in a sixth form college eat sausages for dinner and 20% eat chips.
10% of those who eat chips also eat sausages. By use of a Venn diagram or otherwise, find:
- ***a) the percentage of students who eat both chips and sausages,***
- ***b) the percentage of students who eat chips but not sausages,***
- ***c) the percentage of students who eat either chips or sausages but not both.***

Sample Exam question:

3. A soap company asked 120 people about the types of soap (from Brands A, B and C) they bought. Brand A was bought by 40 people, Brand B by 30 people and Brand C by 25. Both Brands A and B (and possibly C as well) were bought by 8 people, B and C (and maybe A) were bought by 10 people, and A and C (and maybe B) by 7 people. All three brands were bought by 3 people.

(a) Represent this information in a Venn diagram. [5 marks]

(b) If a person is selected at random, find the probability that:
- (i) they buy at least one of the soaps. [2 marks]
- (ii) they buy at least two of the soaps, [2 marks]
- (iii) they buy soap B, given that they buy only one type of soap. [3 marks]

Two heads are better than one — though only half as likely using two coins...

I must admit — I kind of like these pages. This stuff isn't too hard, and it's really useful for answering loads of questions. And one other good thing is that Venn diagrams look, well, nice somehow. But more importantly, when you're filling one in, the thing to remember is that you usually need to 'start from the inside and work out'.

Probability

So far so good. But I can see you want more.

Mutually Exclusive Events Have *No Overlap*

If two events can't both happen at the same time (i.e. $P(A \cap B) = 0$) they're called mutually exclusive (or just 'exclusive').

If A and B are exclusive, then the probability of A or B is: $P(A \cup B) = P(A) + P(B)$. ← Use the formula from page 14, but put $P(A \cap B) = 0$.

More generally,

For n exclusive events (i.e. only one of them can happen at a time):

$$P(A_1 \cup A_2 \cup ... \cup A_n) = P(A_1) + P(A_2) + ... + P(A_n)$$

Example: Find the probability that a card pulled at random from a pack of cards (no jokers) is either a picture card (a Jack, Queen or King) or the 7, 8 or 9 of clubs.

Call event A — 'I get a picture card', and event B — 'I get the 7, 8 or 9 of clubs'.

Events A and B are mutually exclusive — they can't both happen. Also, $P(A) = \frac{12}{52} = \frac{3}{13}$ and $P(B) = \frac{3}{52}$.

So the probability of either A or B is: $P(A \cup B) = P(A) + P(B) = \frac{12}{52} + \frac{3}{52} = \frac{15}{52}$

The *Complement* of 'Event A' is '*Not Event A*'

An event A will either happen or not happen. The event 'A doesn't happen' is called the complement of A (or A'). On a Venn diagram, it would look like this (because $A \cup A' = S$, the sample space):

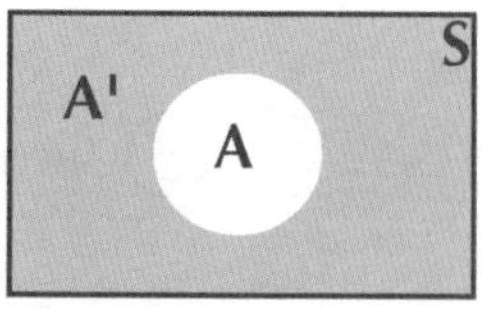

A' A S

At least one of A and A' has to happen, so...

$$P(A) + P(A') = 1 \quad or \quad P(A') = 1 - P(A)$$

Example: A teacher keeps socks loose in a box. One morning, he picks out a sock. He quickly calculates that the probability of then picking out a matching sock is 0.56. What is the probability of him not picking a matching sock?

Call event A 'picks a matching sock'. Then A' is 'doesn't pick a matching sock'. Now A and A' are complementary events (and P(A) = 0.56), so P(A) + P(A') = 1, and therefore P(A') = 1 – 0.56 = 0.44

Tree Diagrams Show Probabilities for *Two or More* Events

Each 'chunk' of a tree diagram is a trial, and each branch of that chunk is a possible outcome. Multiplying probabilities along the branches gives you the probability of a series of outcomes.

Example: If Susan plays tennis one day, the probability that she'll play the next day is 0.2. If she doesn't play tennis, the probability that she'll play the next day is 0.6. She plays tennis on Monday. What is the probability she plays tennis:

(i) on both the Tuesday and Wednesday of that week?
(ii) on the Wednesday of the same week?

Let T mean 'plays tennis' (and then T' means 'doesn't play tennis').

(i) Then the probability that she plays on Tuesday and Wednesday is P(T and T) = 0.2 × 0.2 = 0.04 (multiply probabilities since you need a series of outcomes — T and then T).

(ii) Now you're interested in either P(T and T) or P(T' and T). To find the probability of one event or another happening, you have to add probabilities: P(plays on Wednesday) = 0.04 + 0.48 = 0.52.

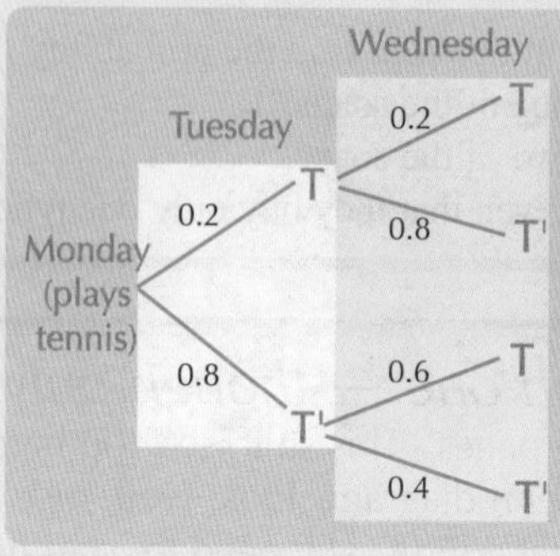

Monday (plays tennis) — Tuesday — Wednesday

0.2 → T: 0.2 → T P(T and T) = 0.2 × 0.2 = 0.04; 0.8 → T' P(T and T') = 0.2 × 0.8 = 0.16

0.8 → T': 0.6 → T P(T' and T) = 0.8 × 0.6 = 0.48; 0.4 → T' P(T' and T') = 0.8 × 0.4 = 0.32

Notice that these add up to 1.

Probability

Sometimes a Branch is *Missing*

Example: A box of biscuits contains 5 chocolate biscuits and 1 lemon biscuit. George takes out 3 biscuits at random, one at a time, and eats them.

a) Find the probability that he eats 3 chocolate biscuits.

b) Find the probability that the last biscuit is chocolate.

Let C mean 'picks a chocolate biscuit' and L mean 'picks the lemon biscuit'.

1st pick — 2nd pick — 3rd pick

$\frac{5}{6}$ C → $\frac{4}{5}$ C → $\frac{3}{4}$ C: $\frac{5}{6}\times\frac{4}{5}\times\frac{3}{4}$

$\frac{5}{6}$ C → $\frac{4}{5}$ C → $\frac{1}{4}$ L: $\frac{5}{6}\times\frac{4}{5}\times\frac{1}{4}$

$\frac{5}{6}$ C → $\frac{1}{5}$ L → 1 C: $\frac{5}{6}\times\frac{1}{5}\times1$

$\frac{1}{6}$ L → 1 C → 1 C: $\frac{1}{6}\times1\times1$

After the lemon biscuit there are only chocolate biscuits left, so the tree diagram doesn't 'branch' after an 'L'.

a) Three chocolate biscuits is shown by only one 'path' along the branches.

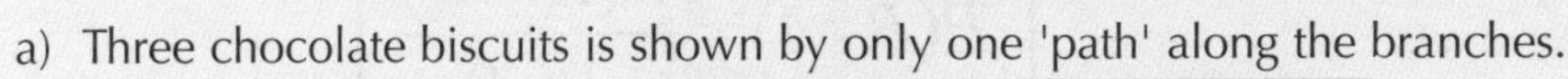

$$P(\text{C and C and C}) = \frac{5}{6}\times\frac{4}{5}\times\frac{3}{4} = \frac{60}{120} = \frac{1}{2}$$

b) The third biscuit being chocolate is shown by 3 'paths' along the branches — so you can add up the probabilities:

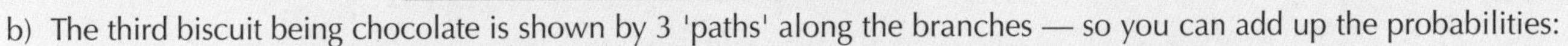

$$P(\text{third biscuit is chocolate}) = \left(\frac{5}{6}\times\frac{4}{5}\times\frac{3}{4}\right)+\left(\frac{5}{6}\times\frac{1}{5}\times1\right)+\left(\frac{1}{6}\times1\times1\right) = \frac{1}{2}+\frac{1}{6}+\frac{1}{6} = \frac{5}{6}$$

There's a quicker way to do this, since there's only one outcome where the chocolate isn't picked last:

$$P(\text{third biscuit is not chocolate}) = \frac{5}{6}\times\frac{4}{5}\times\frac{1}{4} = \frac{1}{6}, \text{ so } P(\text{third biscuit is chocolate}) = 1-\frac{1}{6} = \frac{5}{6}$$

Working out the probability of the complement of the event you're interested in is sometimes easier.

Sampling *with replacement* — the probabilities stay the same

In the above example, each time George takes a biscuit he eats it before taking the next one (i.e. he doesn't replace it) — this is sampling without replacement. Suppose instead that each time he takes a biscuit he puts it back in the box before taking the next one — this is sampling with replacement. All this means is that the probability of choosing a particular item remains the same for each pick.

So part a) above becomes:

$$P(\text{C and C and C}) = \frac{5}{6}\times\frac{5}{6}\times\frac{5}{6} = \frac{125}{216} > \frac{1}{2}$$

So the probability that George picks 3 chocolate biscuits is slightly greater when sampling is done with replacement. This makes sense because now there are more chocolate biscuits available for his 2nd and 3rd picks, so he is more likely to choose one.

Practice Questions

1. ***Arabella rolls two dice and adds the two results together.***
   a) What is the probability that she scores a prime number?
   b) What is the probability that she scores a square number?
   c) What is the probability that she scores a number that is either a prime number or a square number?

2. ***In a school orchestra (made up of pupils in either the upper or lower school), 40% of the musicians are boys. Of the boys, 30% are in the upper school. Of the girls in the orchestra, 50% are in the upper school.***
   a) Draw a tree diagram to show the various probabilities.
   b) Find the probability that a musician chosen at random is in the upper school.

Sample Exam question:

3. A jar contains counters of various colours. There are 3 red counters, 4 white counters and 5 green counters. Two random counters are removed from the jar one at a time. Once removed, the colour of the counter is noted. The first counter is not replaced before the second one is drawn.
   (a) Draw a tree diagram to show the probabilities of the various outcomes. [3 marks]
   (b) Find the probability that the second counter is green. [2 marks]
   (c) Find the probability that both the counters are red. [2 marks]
   (d) Find the probability that the two counters are not both the same colour. [3 marks]

Useful quotes: I can live for two months on a good compliment...*

Tree diagrams are another one of those things that are fairly easy to get your head round, but at the same time, are incredibly useful. And if you get stuck trying to work out a probability, it's worth checking to see if the probability of the complementary event would be easier to find — because if you can find one, then you can easily work out the other.

* Mark Twain

Conditional Probability

Examiners love conditional probability — they can't get enough of it. So learn this well...

P(B|A) means Probability of B, given that A has Already Happened

Conditional probability means the probability of something, given that something else has already happened.
For example, P(B|A) means the probability of B, given that A has already happened. More tree diagrams...

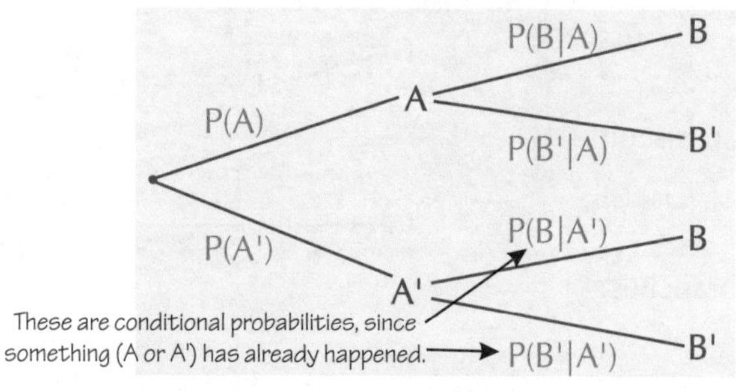

If you multiply probabilities along the branches, you get:

i.e. P(A and B) $\Rightarrow P(A \cap B) = P(A) \times P(B \mid A)$

You can rewrite this as:

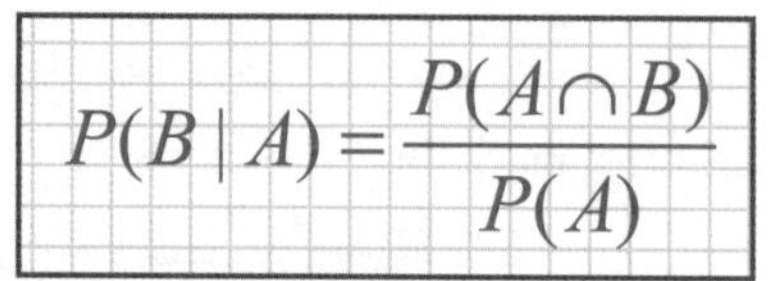

$$P(B \mid A) = \frac{P(A \cap B)}{P(A)}$$

Example: Horace either walks (W) or runs (R) to the bus stop.
If he walks he catches (C) the bus with a probability of 0.3. If he runs he catches it with a probability of 0.7. He walks to the bus stop with a probability of 0.4.
Find the probability that Horace catches the bus.

P(C) = P(C∩W) + P(C∩R)
= P(W)P(C|W) + P(R)P(C|R)
= (0.4 × 0.3) + (0.6 × 0.7) = 0.12 + 0.42 = 0.54

This is easier to follow if you match each part of this working to the probabilities in the tree diagram.

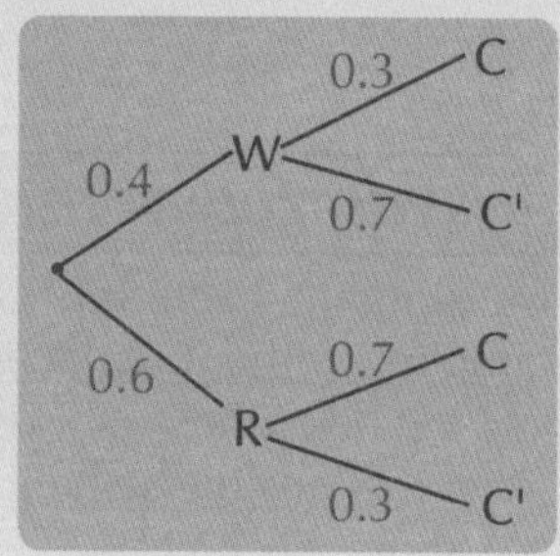

If B is Conditional on A then A is Conditional on B

If B depends on A then A depends on B — and it doesn't matter which event happens first.

Example: Horace turns up at school either late (L) or on time (L'). He is then either shouted at (S) or not (S'). The probability that he turns up late is 0.4. If he turns up late the probability that he is shouted at is 0.7. If he turns up on time the probability that he is shouted at is 0.2.
If you hear Horace being shouted at, what is the probability that he turned up late?

1) The probability you want is P(L|S). Get this the right way round — he's already being shouted at.

2) Use the conditional probability formula: $P(L \mid S) = \frac{P(L \cap S)}{P(S)}$

3) The best way to find $P(L \cap S)$ and $P(S)$ is with a tree diagram.

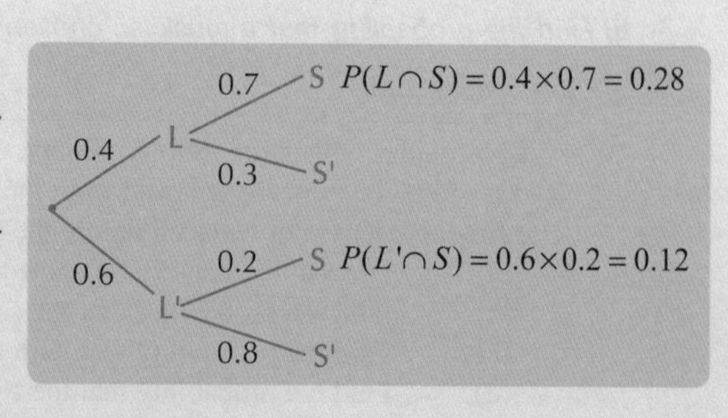

Be careful with questions like this — the information in the question tells you what you need to know to draw the tree diagram with L (or L') considered first. But you need P(L|S) — where S is considered first. So don't just rush in.

$$P(L \cap S) = 0.4 \times 0.7 = 0.28$$
$$P(S) = P(L \cap S) + P(L' \cap S) = 0.28 + 0.12 = 0.40$$

4) Put these in your conditional probability formula to get:

$$P(L \mid S) = \frac{0.28}{0.4} = 0.7$$

Conditional Probability

Independent Events Have *No Effect* on Each Other

If the probability of B happening doesn't depend on whether or not A has happened, then A and B are independent.

1) If A and B are independent, P(A|B) = P(A).
2) If you put this in the conditional probability formula, you get: $P(A|B) = P(A) = \frac{P(A \cap B)}{P(B)}$

Or, to put that another way: For independent events: $P(A \cap B) = P(A)P(B)$

Example: You are exposed to two infectious diseases — one after the other. The probability you catch the first (A) is 0.25, the probability you catch the second (B) is 0.5, and the probability you catch both of them is 0.2. Are catching the two diseases independent events?

1) You need to compare P(A|B) and P(A) — if they're different, the events aren't independent.

$$P(A|B) = \frac{P(A \cap B)}{P(B)} = \frac{0.2}{0.5} = 0.4 \qquad P(A) = 0.25$$

2) P(A|B) and P(A) are different, so they are not independent.

Practice Questions

1. A and B are two events. P(A) = 0.4, P(B) = 0.3, P(A∩B) = 0.1.
a) Find P(B|A).
b) Find P(B|A').
c) Say whether or not A and B are independent.

2. Albert eats a limited choice of lunch. He eats either chicken or beef for his main course, and either chocolate pudding or ice cream for dessert. The probability that he eats chicken is 1/3, the probability that he eats ice cream given that he has chicken is 2/5, and the probability that he has ice cream given that he has beef is 3/4.
a) Find the probability he has either chicken or ice cream — but not both.
b) Find the probability that he eats ice cream.
c) Find the probability that he had chicken given that you see him eating ice cream.

<u>Sample Exam questions</u>:

3. V and W are independent events, where P(V) = 0.2 and P(W) = 0.6.
(a) Find: (i) P(V ∩ W), and (ii) P(V ∪ W). [3 marks]
(b) If U is the event that neither V or W occurs, find P(U|V'). [3 marks]

4. For a particular biased dice, the event 'throw a 6' is called event B. P(B) = 0.2.
This biased dice and a fair dice are rolled together. Find the probability that:
(a) the biased dice doesn't show a 6, [1 mark]
(b) at least one of the dice shows a 6, [2 marks]
(c) exactly one of the dice shows a 6, given that at least one of them shows a 6. [3 marks]

Statisticians say: P(Having cake ∩ Eating it) = 0...

It's very easy to assume that events are independent and use the P(A∩B) formula in the red box on this page — when in fact they're not independent at all and you should be using the formula in the blue box on page 18. I admit that using the wrong formula may make the calculations slightly easier — but think how virtuous you'll feel if you do things the hard way.

Probability Distributions

This stuff isn't hard — but it can seem a bit weird at times.

Getting your head round this **Boring Stuff** will help a bit

This first bit isn't particularly interesting. But understanding the difference between X and x (bear with me) might make the later stuff a bit less confusing. Might.

1) X (upper case) is just the name of a random variable. So X could be 'score on a dice' — it's just a name.
2) A random variable doesn't have a fixed value. Like with a dice score — the value on any 'roll' is all down to chance.
3) x (lower case) is a particular value that X can take. So for one roll of a dice, x could be 1, 2, 3, 4, 5 or 6.

4) Discrete random variables only have a certain number of possible values. Often these values are whole numbers, but they don't have to be. Usually there are only a few possible values (e.g. the possible scores with one roll of a dice).
5) The probability density function, pdf (also called a probability function), is a list of the possible values of x, plus the probability for each one.

All the Probabilities **Add up to 1**

For a discrete random variable X:

$$\sum_{\text{all } x} P(X = x) = 1$$

Example: The random variable X has pdf $P(X = x) = kx$ for $x = 1, 2, 3$. Find the value of k.

So X has three possible values (x = 1, 2 and 3), and the probability of each is kx (where you need to find k).
It's easier to understand with a table:

x	1	2	3
$P(X = x)$	$k \times 1 = k$	$k \times 2 = 2k$	$k \times 3 = 3k$

Now just use the formula: $\sum_{\text{all } x} P(X = x) = 1$ Here, this means: $k + 2k + 3k = 6k = 1$

i.e. $k = \frac{1}{6}$

Piece of cake.

The **mode** is the most likely value — so it's the value with the biggest probability.

Example: The discrete random variable X has pdf as shown in the table below.

x	0	1	2	3	4
$P(X = x)$	0.1	0.2	0.3	0.2	a

Find: (i) the value of a, (ii) $P(2 \leq X < 4)$, (iii) the mode

(i) Use the formula $\sum_{\text{all } x} P(X = x) = 1$ again.

From the table: $0.1 + 0.2 + 0.3 + 0.2 + a = 1$
$0.8 + a = 1$
$a = 0.2$

Careful with the inequality signs — you need to include $x = 2$ but not $x = 4$.

(ii) This is asking for the probability that 'X is greater than or equal to 2, but less than 4'. Easy — just add up the probabilities.

$P(2 \leq X < 4) = P(X = 2) + P(X = 3) = 0.3 + 0.2 = 0.5$

(iii) The mode is the value of x with the biggest probability — so mode = 2.

Probability Distributions

Do Complicated questions Bit by bit

Example: A game involves rolling two fair dice. If the sum of the scores is greater than 10 then the player wins 50p. If the sum is between 8 and 10 (inclusive) then he wins 20p. Otherwise he gets nothing. If X is the random variable "amount player wins", find the pdf of X.

There are 3 possible values for X (0, 20 and 50) and you need the probability of each. To work these out, you need the probability of getting various totals on the dice.

1. You need to know $P(8 \leq \text{score} \leq 10)$ — the probability that the score is between 8 and 10 inclusive (i.e. including 8 and 10) and $P(11 \leq \text{score} \leq 12)$ — the probability that the score is greater than 10.

   This means working out: P(score = 8), P(score = 9), P(score = 10), P(score = 11) and P(score = 12). Use a table...

2. Score on dice 1 (columns) / Score on dice 2 (rows)

+	1	2	3	4	5	6
1	2	3	4	5	6	7
2	3	4	5	6	7	8
3	4	5	6	7	8	9
4	5	6	7	8	9	10
5	6	7	8	9	10	11
6	7	8	9	10	11	12

There are 36 possible outcomes...

...5 of these have a total of 8 — so the probability of scoring 8 is $\frac{5}{36}$,

...4 have a total of 9 — so the probability of scoring 9 is $\frac{4}{36}$,

...the probability of scoring 10 is $\frac{3}{36}$

...the probability of scoring 11 is $\frac{2}{36}$

...the probability of scoring 12 is $\frac{1}{36}$

3. To find the probabilities you need, you just add the right bits together:

$$P(X = 20p) = P(8 \leq \text{score} \leq 10) = \frac{5}{36}+\frac{4}{36}+\frac{3}{36}=\frac{12}{36}=\frac{1}{3}$$

$$P(X = 50p) = P(11 \leq \text{score} \leq 12) = \frac{2}{36}+\frac{1}{36}=\frac{3}{36}=\frac{1}{12}$$

To find P(X = 0) just take the total of the two probabilities above from 1 (since X = 0 is the only other possibility).

$$P(X = 0) = 1-\left[\frac{12}{36}+\frac{3}{36}\right]=1-\frac{15}{36}=\frac{21}{36}=\frac{7}{12}$$

4. Now just stick all this info in a table (and check that the probabilities all add up to 1):

x	0	20	50
$P(X = x)$	$\frac{7}{12}$	$\frac{1}{3}$	$\frac{1}{12}$

Practice Questions

1) The probability density function of Y is shown in the table.
(a) Find the value of k. (b) Find P(Y<2).

y	0	1	2	3
$P(Y = y)$	0.5	k	k	3k

2) An unbiased six-sided dice has faces marked 1, 1, 1, 2, 2, 3.
The dice is rolled twice. Let X be the random variable "sum of the two scores on the dice".

Show that $P(X = 4) = \frac{5}{18}$. Find the probability density function of X.

Sample exam question:

3) In a game a player tosses three fair coins. If three heads occur then the player gets 20p; if two heads occur then the player gets 10p; otherwise the player gets nothing.

(a) If X is the random variable 'amount received' tabulate the probability density function of X. [4 marks]

The player pays 10p to play one game.

(b) Use the probability density function to find the probability that the player wins (i.e. gets more money than he pays to play) in one game. [2 marks]

Useful quotes: All you need in life is ignorance and confidence, then success is sure...*

Remember I said earlier that the 'counting the outcomes' approach was useful — well there you go. And if you remember how to do that, then you can work out a pdf. And if you can work out a pdf, then you can often begin to unravel even fairly daunting-looking questions. But most of all, REMEMBER THAT ALL THE PROBABILITIES ADD UP TO 1. (Ahem.)

* Mark Twain

The Distribution Function

The pdf gives the probability that X will equal this or equal that. The distribution function tells you something else.

'Distribution Function' is the same as 'Cumulative Distribution Function'

The (cumulative) distribution function F(x) gives the probability that X will be less than or equal to a particular value.

$$F(x_0) = P(X \leq x_0) = \sum_{x \leq x_0} p(x)$$

Example: The probability density function of the discrete random variable H is shown in the table. Find the cumulative distribution function F(h).

h	0.1	0.2	0.3	0.4
$P(H = h)$	$\frac{1}{4}$	$\frac{1}{4}$	$\frac{1}{3}$	$\frac{1}{6}$

There are 4 values of h, so you have to find the probability that H is less than or equal to each of them in turn. It sounds trickier than it actually is — you only have to add up a few probabilities...

$F(0.1) = P(H \leq 0.1)$ — this is the same as $P(H = 0.1)$, since H can't be less than 0.1. So $F(0.1) = \frac{1}{4}$.

$F(0.2) = P(H \leq 0.2)$ — this is the probability that H = 0.1 or H = 0.2. So $F(0.2) = P(H = 0.1) + P(H = 0.2) = \frac{1}{4} + \frac{1}{4} = \frac{1}{2}$.

$F(0.3) = P(H \leq 0.3) = P(H = 0.1) + P(H = 0.2) + P(H = 0.3) = \frac{1}{4} + \frac{1}{4} + \frac{1}{3} = \frac{5}{6}$.

$F(0.4) = P(H \leq 0.4) = P(H = 0.1) + P(H = 0.2) + P(H = 0.3) + P(H = 0.4) = \frac{1}{4} + \frac{1}{4} + \frac{1}{3} + \frac{1}{6} = 1$.

P(X ≤ largest value of x) is always 1.

Finally, put these values in a table, and you're done...

h	0.1	0.2	0.3	0.4
$F(h) = P(H \leq h)$	$\frac{1}{4}$	$\frac{1}{2}$	$\frac{5}{6}$	1

Sometimes they ask you to work backwards...

Example: The formula below gives the cumulative distribution function F(x) for a discrete random variable X. Find k, and the probability density function.

$F(x) = kx$, for $x = 1, 2, 3$ and 4.

1. First find k. You know that X has to be 4 or less — so $P(X \leq 4) = 1$.

   Put x = 4 into the cumulative distribution function: $F(4) = P(X \leq 4) = 4k = 1$, so $k = \frac{1}{4}$.

2. Now you can work out the probabilities of X being less than or equal to 1, 2, 3 and 4.

   $F(1) = P(X \leq 1) = 1 \times k = \frac{1}{4}$, $F(2) = P(X \leq 2) = 2 \times k = \frac{1}{2}$, $F(3) = P(X \leq 3) = 3 \times k = \frac{3}{4}$, $F(4) = P(X \leq 4) = 1$

3. This is the clever bit... $P(X = 4) = P(X \leq 4) - P(X \leq 3) = 1 - \frac{3}{4} = \frac{1}{4}$

   Think about it... ...if it's less than or equal to 4, ...but it's not less than or equal to 3, ...then it has to be 4.

   $P(X = 3) = P(X \leq 3) - P(X \leq 2) = \frac{3}{4} - \frac{1}{2} = \frac{1}{4}$

   $P(X = 2) = P(X \leq 2) - P(X \leq 1) = \frac{1}{2} - \frac{1}{4} = \frac{1}{4}$

   $P(X = 1) = P(X \leq 1) = \frac{1}{4}$

   Because x doesn't take any values less than 1.

4. Finish it all off by making a table. The pdf of X is:

x	1	2	3	4
$P(X = x)$	$\frac{1}{4}$	$\frac{1}{4}$	$\frac{1}{4}$	$\frac{1}{4}$

Or you could write it as a formula: $P(X = x) = \frac{1}{4}$ for $x = 1, 2, 3, 4$

Discrete Uniform Distributions

When every value of X is equally likely, you've got a uniform distribution. For example, rolling an unbiased dice gives you a discrete uniform distribution. (It's 'discrete' because there are only a few possible outcomes.)

In a Discrete Uniform Distribution the Probabilities are Equal

The pdf of a discrete uniform distribution looks like this — in this version there are only 4 possible values:

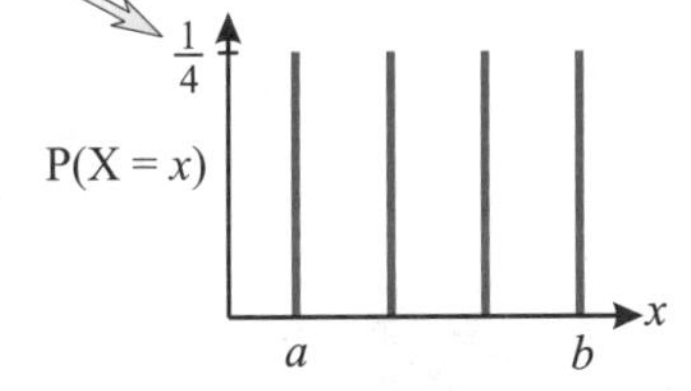

For a discrete uniform distribution X which can take consecutive whole number values a, a+1, a+2,...,b, the mean (or expected value) and variance are easy to work out.

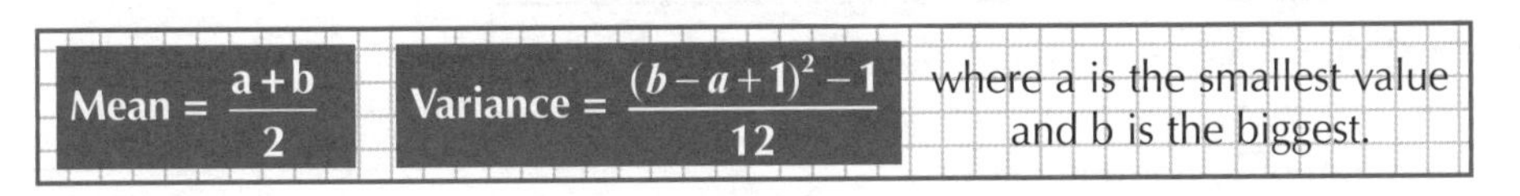

See page 24 for more info about the expected value and variance of a random variable.

Example: Find the mean and variance of the score on an unbiased six-sided dice.

If X is the random variable 'score on a dice', then X has a discrete uniform distribution — like in this table:

x	1	2	3	4	5	6
P(X = x)	$\frac{1}{6}$	$\frac{1}{6}$	$\frac{1}{6}$	$\frac{1}{6}$	$\frac{1}{6}$	$\frac{1}{6}$

The symmetry of the distribution should tell you where the mean is — it has to be halfway between 1 and 6.

The smallest value of x is 1 and the biggest is 6 — so a = 1 and b = 6.
Now just stick the numbers in the formulas:

Mean = $\frac{a+b}{2} = \frac{1+6}{2} = \frac{7}{2} = \underline{3.5}$

Variance = $\frac{(b-a+1)^2-1}{12} = \frac{(6-1+1)^2-1}{12} = \frac{35}{12} = \underline{2.92}$ to 3 sig. fig.

Practice Questions

1) The probability density function for the random variable W is given in the table. Find the cumulative distribution function.

w	0.2	0.3	0.4	0.5
P(W = w)	0.2	0.2	0.3	0.3

2) The cumulative distribution function for a random variable R is given in the table. Calculate the probability density function for R. Find P(0 ≤ R ≤ 1).

r	0	1	2
F(r) = P(R ≤ r)	0.1	0.5	1

3) The discrete random variable X has a uniform distribution, P(X = x) = k for x = 0, 1, 2, 3 and 4. Find the value of k, and then find the mean and variance of X.

Sample exam questions:

4) A discrete random variable X can only take values 0, 1, 2 and 3. Its pdf is shown in the table.

x	0	1	2	3
P(X = x)	$2k$	$3k$	k	k

(a) Find the value of k. [1 mark]
(b) Calculate the distribution function for X. [4 marks]
(c) Calculate P(X > 2). [1 mark]

5) The random variable X takes the values 0, 1, 2, 3, 4, 5, 6, 7, 8 and 9 with equal probability.

(a) Write down the pdf of X. [1 mark]
(b) Find the mean and variance of X. [3 marks]
(c) Calculate the probability that X is less than the mean. [2 marks]

Discreet distributions are more 'British' than those lurid, gaudy ones...

If you've got a pdf, then you can easily work out the distribution function. And if you've got a distribution function, you can work out the pdf, as long as you remember the clever wee trick on page 22. The mean of a discrete uniform distribution is weird. I mean (no stats-pun intended), if you've got a dice, then the expected value is 3½. But I went to a casino recently and bet on 3½ every time at the 'Guess the Dice' table. But not once did the dice ever land on 3½. Not once. I lost loads.

Expected Values, Mean and Variance

This is all about the mean and variance of random variables — not a load of data. It's a tricky concept, but bear with it.

The *Mean* of a random variable is the same as the *Expected Value*

You can work out the expected value (or the mean) E(X) of a random variable X.

The expected value (a kind of 'theoretical mean') is what you'd expect the mean of X to be if you took loads of readings. In practice, the mean of your results is unlikely to match the theoretical mean exactly, but it should be pretty near.

If the possible values of X are $x_1, x_2, x_3, \ldots$ then the expected value of X is:

$$\text{Mean} = \text{Expected Value } E(X) = \sum x_i P(X = x_i) = \sum x_i p_i$$

$p_i = P(X = x_i)$

Example: The probability distribution of X, the number of daughters in a family of 3 children, is shown in the table. Find the expected number of daughters.

x_i	0	1	2	3
p_i	$\frac{1}{8}$	$\frac{3}{8}$	$\frac{3}{8}$	$\frac{1}{8}$

$$\text{Mean} = \sum x_i p_i = \left[0 \times \tfrac{1}{8}\right] + \left[1 \times \tfrac{3}{8}\right] + \left[2 \times \tfrac{3}{8}\right] + \left[3 \times \tfrac{1}{8}\right] = 0 + \tfrac{3}{8} + \tfrac{6}{8} + \tfrac{3}{8} = \tfrac{12}{8} = 1.5$$

So the expected number of daughters is 1.5 — which sounds a bit weird.
But all it means is that if you check a large number of 3-child families, the mean will be close to 1.5.

The *Variance* measures how *Spread Out* the distribution is

You can also find the variance of a random variable. It's the 'expected variance' of a large number of readings.

$$\text{Var}(X) = E(X^2) - [E(X)]^2 = \sum x_i^2 p_i - \left[\sum x_i p_i\right]^2$$

This formula needs $E(X^2) = \sum x_i^2 p_i$ — take each possible value of x, square it, multiply it by its probability and then add up all the results.

Example: Work out the variance for the '3 daughters' example above:

First work out $E(X^2)$: $E(X^2) = \sum x_i^2 p_i = \left[0^2 \times \tfrac{1}{8}\right] + \left[1^2 \times \tfrac{3}{8}\right] + \left[2^2 \times \tfrac{3}{8}\right] + \left[3^2 \times \tfrac{1}{8}\right]$
$= 0 + \tfrac{3}{8} + \tfrac{12}{8} + \tfrac{9}{8} = \tfrac{24}{8} = 3$

Now you take away the mean squared: $\text{Var}(X) = E(X^2) - [E(X)]^2 = 3 - 1.5^2 = 3 - 2.25 = 0.75$

Example: X has the probability density function $P(X = x) = k(x + 1)$ for $x = 0, 1, 2, 3, 4$.
Find the mean and variance of X.

① First you need to find k — work out all the probabilities and make sure they add up to 1.
$P(X = 0) = k \times (0 + 1) = k$. Similarly, $P(X = 1) = 2k$, $P(X = 2) = 3k$, $P(X = 3) = 4k$, $P(X = 4) = 5k$.

So $k + 2k + 3k + 4k + 5k = 1$, i.e. $15k = 1$, and so $k = \frac{1}{15}$

Now you can work out $p_1, p_2, p_3, \ldots$ where $p_1 = P(X = 1)$ etc.

② Now use the formulas — find the mean E(X) first:

$$E(X) = \sum x_i p_i = \left[0 \times \tfrac{1}{15}\right] + \left[1 \times \tfrac{2}{15}\right] + \left[2 \times \tfrac{3}{15}\right] + \left[3 \times \tfrac{4}{15}\right] + \left[4 \times \tfrac{5}{15}\right] = \tfrac{40}{15} = \tfrac{8}{3}$$

For the variance you need $E(X^2)$:

$$E(X^2) = \sum x_i^2 p_i = \left[0^2 \times \tfrac{1}{15}\right] + \left[1^2 \times \tfrac{2}{15}\right] + \left[2^2 \times \tfrac{3}{15}\right] + \left[3^2 \times \tfrac{4}{15}\right] + \left[4^2 \times \tfrac{5}{15}\right] = \tfrac{130}{15} = \tfrac{26}{3}$$

And finally: $Var(X) = E(X^2) - [E(X)]^2 = \frac{26}{3} - \left[\frac{8}{3}\right]^2 = \frac{14}{9}$

Expected Values, Mean and Variance

You can use the *Expected Value* and *Variance* formulas for *Functions*

$E(aX + b) = aE(X) + b$ **$Var(aX + b) = a^2Var(X)$**

Here a and b are any numbers.

Example: If E(X) = 3 and Var(X) = 7, find E(2X+5) and Var(2X+5).

Easy. $E(2X + 5) = 2E(X) + 5 = (2 \times 3) + 5 = 11$

$Var(2X + 5) = 2^2Var(X) = 4 \times 7 = 28$

Example: The discrete random variable X has the following probability distribution:

x	2	3	4	5	6
$P(X = x)$	0.1	0.2	0.3	0.2	k

Find: a) k, b) E(X), c) Var(X), d) E(3X – 1), e) Var(3X – 1)

Slowly, slowly — one bit at a time...

a) Remember the probabilities add up to 1 — $0.1 + 0.2 + 0.3 + 0.2 + k = 1$, and so $k = 0.2$

b) Now you can use the formula to find E(X): $E(X) = \sum x_i p_i = (2 \times 0.1) + (3 \times 0.2) + (4 \times 0.3) + (5 \times 0.2) + (6 \times 0.2) = 4.2$

c) Next work out E(X²): $E(X^2) = \sum x_i^2 p_i = [2^2 \times 0.1] + [3^2 \times 0.2] + [4^2 \times 0.3] + [5^2 \times 0.2] + [6^2 \times 0.2] = 19.2$

and then the variance is easy: $Var(X) = E(X^2) - [E(X)]^2 = 19.2 - 4.2^2 = 1.56$

d) You'd expect the question to get harder but it doesn't: $E(3X - 1) = 3E(X) - 1 = 3 \times 4.2 - 1 = 11.6$

e) And finally: $Var(3X - 1) = 3^2Var(X) = 9 \times 1.56 = 14.04$

Practice Questions

1) *A discrete random variable X has the probability distribution shown in the table, where k is a constant.*

x_i	1	2	3	4
p_i	$\frac{1}{6}$	$\frac{1}{2}$	k	$\frac{5}{24}$

a) Find the value of k.
b) Find E(X) and show Var(X) = 63/64
c) Find E(2X – 1) and Var(2X – 1)

Sample exam question:

2) A discrete random variable X has the pdf $P(X = x) = ax$ for $x = 1, 2, 3$, where a is a constant.

(a) Show $a = \frac{1}{6}$. [1 mark]

(b) Find E(X). [2 marks]

(c) If $Var(X) = \frac{5}{9}$ find E(X²). [2 marks]

(d) Find E(3X + 4) and Var(3X + 4). [3 marks]

Statisticians say: E(Bird in hand) = E(2 Birds in bush)...

The mean and variance here are theoretical values — don't get them confused with the mean and variance of a load of practical observations. This 'theoretical' variance has a similar formula to the variance formula on p8, though — it's just "E(X-squared) minus E(X)-squared". And you can still take the square root of the variance to get the standard deviation.

The Normal Distribution

The normal distribution is everywhere in statistics. Everywhere, I tell you. So learn this well...

For **Continuous** Distributions, **Area = Probability**

1) With discrete random variables, there are 'gaps' between the possible values (see page 23).
2) Continuous random variables are different — there are no gaps.
3) So for a continuous random variable, you can draw the probability density function (pdf) $f(x)$ as a line or curve.
4) The probability of the random variable taking a value between two limits is the area under the graph between those limits.
5) This means that for any single value b, $P(X = b) = 0$. (Since the area under a graph at a single point is zero).
6) This also means that $P(X \leq a)$ (or $P(X < a)$) is the area under the graph to the left of a. And $P(X \geq b)$ is the area to the right of b.
7) Since the total probability is 1, the total area under a pdf must also be 1.

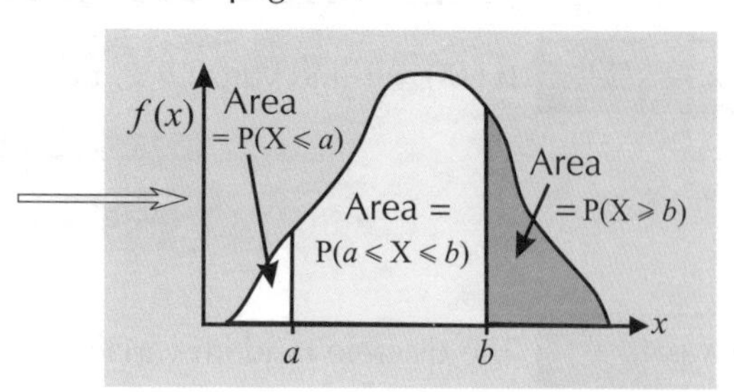

The Normal Distribution has a **Peak** in the **Middle**

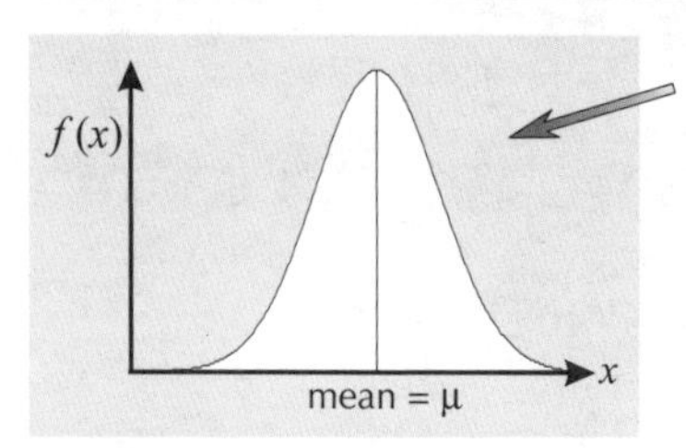

1) A random variable with a normal distribution has a pdf like this — a symmetrical bell-shaped curve.
2) The peak in the centre is at the mean (or expected value). The peak in the pdf tells you that values near the mean are most likely.
3) Further from the mean, the pdf falls — so values far from the mean are less likely.
4) The graph is symmetrical — so values the same distance above and below the mean are equally likely.
5) If X is normally distributed with **mean** μ and **variance** σ^2, it's written $\mathbf{X \sim N(\mu, \sigma^2)}$.

Use **Normal Distribution Tables** and a **Sketch** to find probabilities

This is the practical bit.

1) Working out the area under a normal distribution curve is usually hard. But for the normally-distributed random variable Z, where $\mathbf{Z \sim N(0, 1)}$ (Z has mean 0 and variance 1), there are tables you can use.
2) You look up a value of z and these tables (usually labelled $\Phi(z)$) tell you the probability that $Z \leq z$ (which is the area under the curve to the left of z).
3) You can convert any normally-distributed variable to Z by subtracting the mean and dividing by the standard deviation — this is called normalising. This means that if you normalise a variable, you can use the Z-tables.

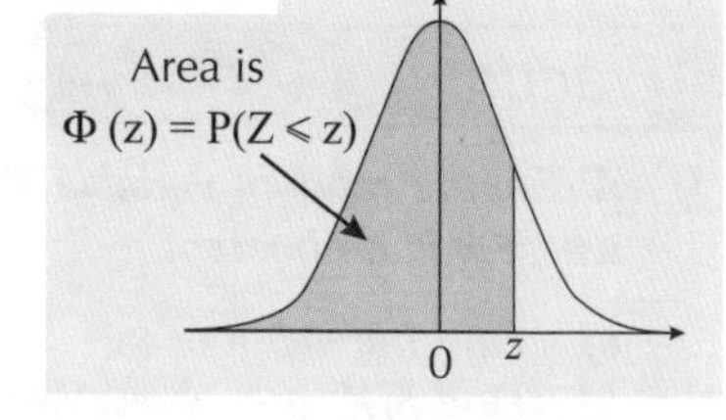

If $X \sim N(\mu, \sigma^2)$, then $\frac{X - \mu}{\sigma} = Z$, where $Z \sim N(0, 1)$

This means that if you subtract μ from any numbers in the question and then divide by σ — you can use your tables for Z.

Example: If $X \sim N(5, 16)$ find a) $P(X < 7)$, b) $P(X > 9)$, c) $P(5 < X < 11)$

Subtract μ (= 5) from any numbers and divide by σ (= $\sqrt{16} = 4$) — then you'll have a probability for $Z \sim N(0, 1)$.

N(5, 16) means the variance is 16 — take the square root to find the standard deviation.

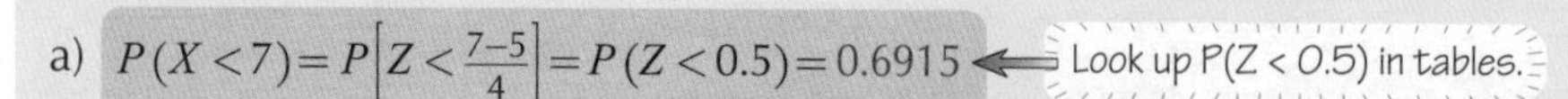

a) $P(X < 7) = P\left[Z < \frac{7-5}{4}\right] = P(Z < 0.5) = 0.6915$

Look up P(Z < 0.5) in tables.

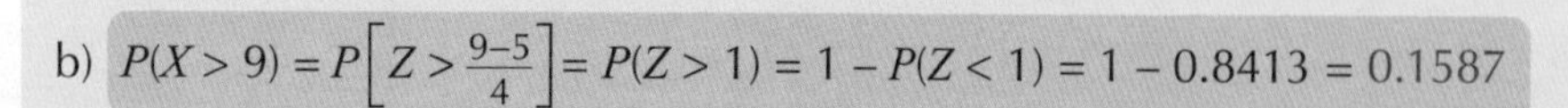

b) $P(X > 9) = P\left[Z > \frac{9-5}{4}\right] = P(Z > 1) = 1 - P(Z < 1) = 1 - 0.8413 = 0.1587$

c) $P(5 < X < 11) = P\left[\frac{5-5}{4} < Z < \frac{11-5}{4}\right] = P(0 < Z < 1.5) = P(Z < 1.5) - P(Z < 0)$

$= 0.9332 - 0.5 = 0.4332$

Find the area to the left of 1.5 and subtract the area to the left of 0.

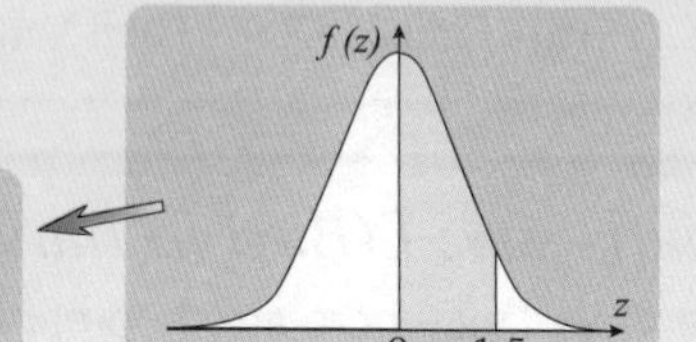

The Normal Distribution

You need to practise loads of questions with the kind of tables you'll be using in the Exam.
Practice makes perfect, as they say.

Draw a Sketch with Normal Probability Questions

There's usually a 'percentage points' table to help you work backwards — use it to answer questions like: How big is k if P(Z < k) = 0.3?

Example: $X \sim N(53, \sigma^2)$ and $P(X < 50) = 0.2$. Find σ.

It's a normal distribution — so your first thought should be to try and normalise it.

① Subtract the mean and divide by the standard deviation:

$$P(X < 50) = P\left[Z < \frac{50-53}{\sigma}\right] = P\left[Z < -\frac{3}{\sigma}\right] = 0.2$$

Ideally, you'd look up 0.2 in the percentage points table to find $-\frac{3}{\sigma}$.
Unfortunately, in some tables it just ain't there, so you have to think a bit...

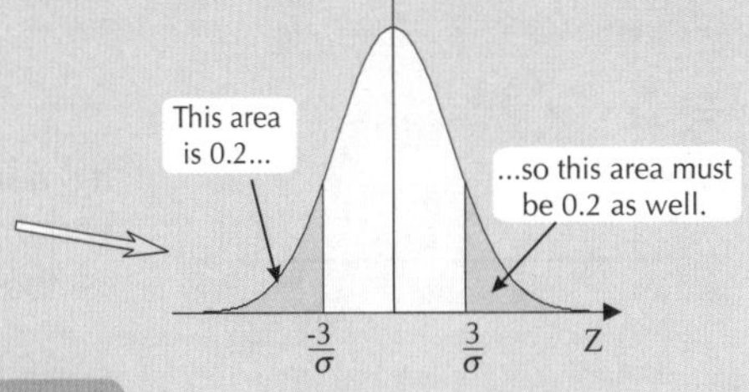

② $P\left[Z < -\frac{3}{\sigma}\right]$ is 0.2, so from the symmetry of the graph, $P\left[Z < \frac{3}{\sigma}\right]$ must be 0.8.

So look up 0.8 in the 'percentage points' table to find that an area of 0.8 is to the left of z = 0.8416.

This tells you that $\frac{3}{\sigma} = 0.8416$, or $\sigma = 3.56$ (to 3 sig. fig.)

Practice Questions

1) If $X \sim N(50, 16)$ find
(a) $P(X < 55)$, (b) $P(X < 42)$, (c) $P(X > 56)$ and (d) $P(47 < X < 57)$.

2) $X \sim N(600, 202)$
(a) If $P(X < a) = 0.95$, find a.
(b) If $P(|X - 600| < b) = 0.8$, find b.

Sample exam questions:

3) The exam marks of 1000 candidates are normally distributed with mean 50 marks and standard deviation 30 marks.
(a) The pass mark is 41. Estimate the number of candidates who passed the exam. [3 marks]
(b) Find the mark required for an A-grade if 10% of the candidates achieved a grade A. [3 marks]

4) The lifetimes of a particular type of battery are normally distributed with mean μ and standard deviation σ.
A student using these batteries finds that 40% last less than 20 hours and 80% last less than 30 hours.
Find μ and σ. [7 marks]

The Medium of a random variable follows a paranormal distribution...

Remember... it's definitely worth drawing a quick sketch when you're finding probabilities using a normal distribution — you're much less likely to make a daft mistake. Also, remember that it's $N(\mu, \sigma^2)$ — with the variance in the brackets and not the standard deviation. This topic isn't too bad once you're happy using the tables. So get hold of some and practise.

Correlation

Correlation is all about how closely two quantities are linked. And it can involve a fairly hefty formula.

*Draw a **Scatter Diagram** to see **Patterns** in Data*

Sometimes variables are measured in pairs — maybe because you want to find out how closely they're linked.
These pairs of variables might be things like: — 'my age' and 'length of my feet', or
— 'temperature' and 'number of accidents on a stretch of road'.

You can plot readings from a pair of variables on a scatter diagram — this'll tell you something about the data.

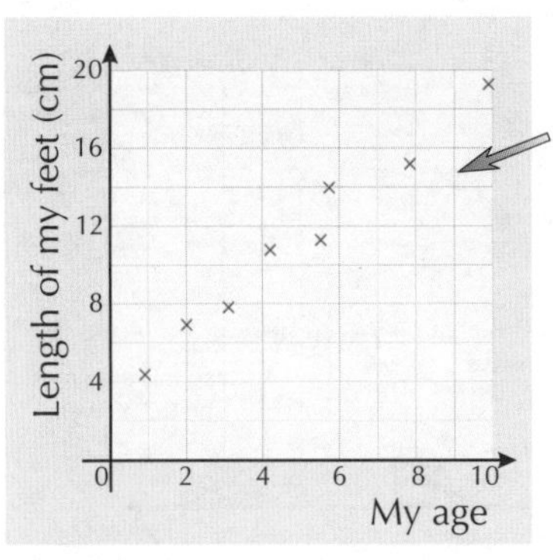

The variables 'my age' and 'length of my feet' seem linked — all the points lie close to a line. As I got older, my feet got bigger and bigger (though I stopped measuring when I was 10).

It's a lot harder to see any connection between the variables 'temperature' and 'number of accidents' — the data seems scattered pretty much everywhere.

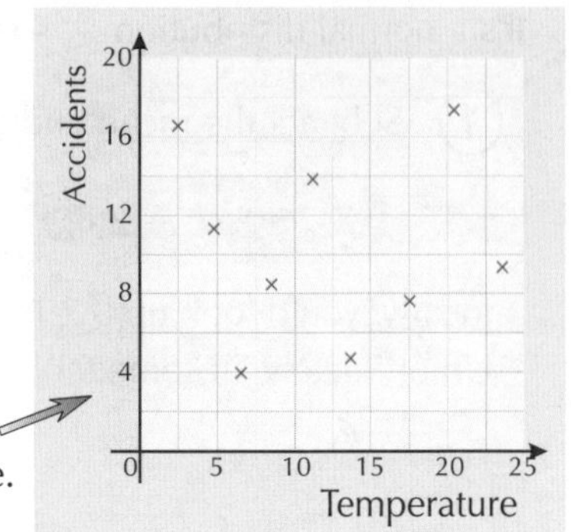

__Correlation__ is a measure of __How Closely__ variables are __Linked__

1) Sometimes, as one variable gets bigger, the other one also gets bigger — then the scatter diagram might look like the one on the right. Here, a line of best fit would have a positive gradient. The two variables are positively correlated (or there's a positive correlation between them).

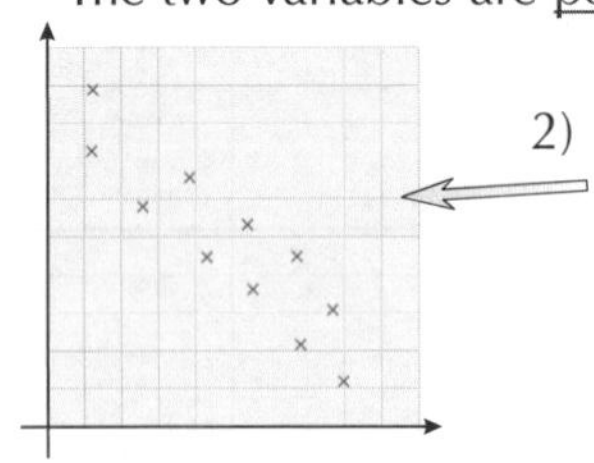

2) But if one variable gets smaller as the other one gets bigger, then the scatter diagram might look like this one — and the line of best fit would have a negative gradient. The two variables are negatively correlated (or there's a negative correlation between them).

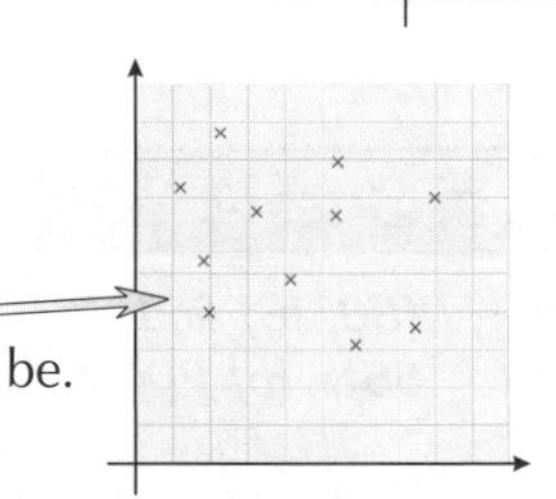

3) And if the two variables aren't linked at all, you'd expect a random scattering of points — it's hard to say where the line of best fit would be. The variables aren't correlated (or there's no correlation).

*The **Product-Moment Correlation Coefficient (r)** measures Correlation*

1) The Product-Moment Correlation Coefficient (PMCC, or r, for short) measures how close to a straight line the points on a scatter graph lie.
2) The PMCC is always between +1 and –1.
If all your points lie exactly on a straight line with a positive gradient (perfect positive correlation), r = +1.
If all your points lie exactly on a straight line with a negative gradient (perfect negative correlation), r = –1.
(In reality, you'd never expect to get a PMCC of +1 or –1 — your scatter graph points might lie pretty close to a straight line, but it's unlikely they'd all be on it.)
3) If r = 0 (or more likely, pretty close to 0), that would mean the variables aren't correlated.
4) The formula for the PMCC is a real stinker. But some calculators can work it out if you type in the pairs of readings, which makes life easier. Otherwise, just take it nice and slow.

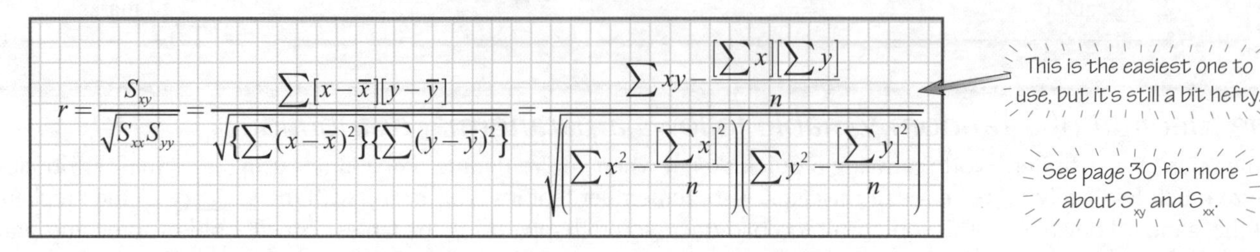

Correlation

Don't rush questions on correlation. In fact, take your time and draw yourself a nice table.

Example: Illustrate the following data with a scatter diagram, and find the product-moment correlation coefficient (r) between the variables x and y. If p = 4x – 3 and q = 9y + 17, what is the PMCC between p and q?

x	1.6	2.0	2.1	2.1	2.5	2.8	2.9	3.3	3.4	3.8	4.1	4.4
y	11.4	11.8	11.5	12.2	12.5	12.0	12.9	13.4	12.8	13.4	14.2	14.3

1) The scatter diagram's the easy bit — just plot the points.

Now for the correlation coefficient. From the scatter diagram, the points lie pretty close to a straight line with a positive gradient — so if the correlation coefficient doesn't come out pretty close to +1, we'd need to worry...

2) There are 12 pairs of readings, so n = 12. That bit's easy — now you have to work out a load of sums. It's best to add a few extra rows to your table...

x	1.6	2	2.1	2.1	2.5	2.8	2.9	3.3	3.4	3.8	4.1	4.4	$35 = \Sigma x$
y	11.4	11.8	11.5	12.2	12.5	12	12.9	13.4	12.8	13.4	14.2	14.3	$152.4 = \Sigma y$
x^2	2.56	4	4.41	4.41	6.25	7.84	8.41	10.89	11.56	14.44	16.81	19.36	$110.94 = \Sigma x^2$
y^2	129.96	139.24	132.25	148.84	156.25	144	166.41	179.56	163.84	179.56	201.64	204.49	$1946.04 = \Sigma y^2$
xy	18.24	23.6	24.15	25.62	31.25	33.6	37.41	44.22	43.52	50.92	58.22	62.92	$453.67 = \Sigma xy$

Stick all these in the formula to get:

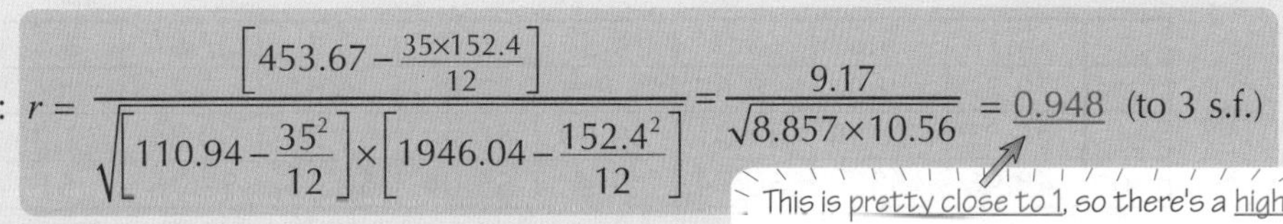

$$r = \frac{\left[453.67 - \frac{35 \times 152.4}{12}\right]}{\sqrt{\left[110.94 - \frac{35^2}{12}\right] \times \left[1946.04 - \frac{152.4^2}{12}\right]}} = \frac{9.17}{\sqrt{8.857 \times 10.56}} = 0.948 \text{ (to 3 s.f.)}$$

3) Correlation coefficients aren't affected by linear transformations — you can multiply variables by a number, and add a number to them — and you won't change the PMCC between them. So if p and q are given by p = 4x – 3 and q = 9y + 17, then the PMCC between p and q is also 0.948.

Don't make *Sweeping Statements* using Statistics

1) A high correlation coefficient doesn't necessarily mean that one quantity causes the other.

Example: The number of televisions sold in Japan and the number of cars sold in America may well be correlated, but that doesn't mean that high TV sales in Japan cause high car sales in the US.

2) The PMCC is only a measure of a linear relationship between two variables (i.e. how close they'd be to a line if you plotted a scatter diagram).

Example: In the diagram on the right, the PMCC would probably be pretty low, but the two variables definitely look linked. It looks like the points lie on a parabola (the shape of an x^2 curve) — not a line.

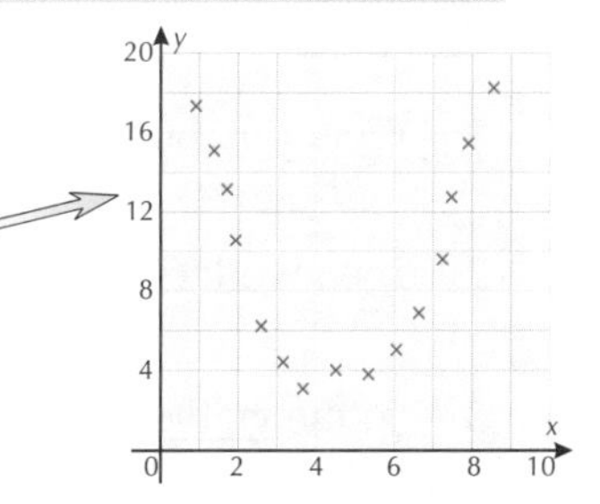

Practice Question

Sample Exam Question:

1. Values of two variables x and y obtained from a survey are recorded in the table below.

x	1	2	3	4	5	6	7	8
y	0.50	0.70	0.10	0.82	0.64	0.36	0.16	0.80

Represent these data on a scatter diagram, and obtain the product-moment correlation coefficient (PMCC) between the two variables. What does this tell you about the variables? [9 marks]

What's a statistician's favourite soap — Correlation Street... (Boom boom)

It's worth remembering that the PMCC assumes that both variables are normally distributed — chances are you won't get asked a question about that, but there's always the possibility that you might, so learn it.

Linear Regression

Linear regression is just fancy stats-speak for 'finding lines of best fit'. Not so scary now, eh...

Decide which is the ***Independent Variable*** and which is the ***Dependent***

Example: The data below show the load on a lorry, x (in tonnes), and the fuel consumption, y (in km per litre).

x	5.1	5.6	5.9	6.3	6.8	7.4	7.8	8.5	9.1	9.8
y	9.6	9.5	8.6	8.0	7.8	6.8	6.7	6	5.4	5.4

1) The variable along the x-axis is the explanatory or independent variable — it's the variable you can control, or the one that you think is affecting the other.
   The variable 'load' goes along the x-axis here.
2) The variable up the y-axis is the response or dependent variable — it's the variable you think is being affected.
   In this example, this is the fuel consumption.

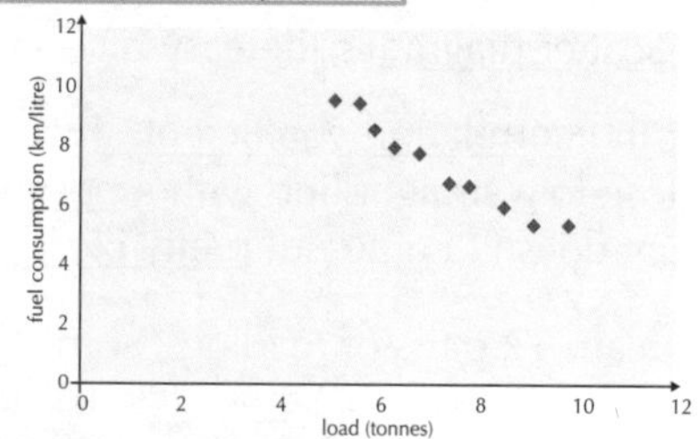

The ***Regression Line*** (Line of Best Fit) is in the form ***y = a + bx***

To find the line of best fit for the above data you need to work out some sums.
Then it's quite easy to work out the equation of the line. If your line of best fit is $y = a + bx$, this is what you do...

① First work out these four sums — a table is probably the best way: $\sum x$, $\sum y$, $\sum x^2$, $\sum xy$.

x	5.1	5.6	5.9	6.3	6.8	7.4	7.8	8.5	9.1	9.8	$72.3 = \Sigma x$
y	9.6	9.5	8.6	8	7.8	6.8	6.7	6	5.4	5.4	$73.8 = \Sigma y$
x^2	26.01	31.36	34.81	39.69	46.24	54.76	60.84	72.25	82.81	96.04	$544.81 = \Sigma x^2$
xy	48.96	53.2	50.74	50.4	53.04	50.32	52.26	51	49.14	52.92	$511.98 = \Sigma xy$

② Then work out S_{xy}, given by: $S_{xy} = \sum(x-\bar{x})(y-\bar{y}) = \sum xy - \frac{(\sum x)(\sum y)}{n}$

and S_{xx}, given by: $S_{xx} = \sum[x-\bar{x}]^2 = \sum x^2 - \frac{(\sum x)^2}{n}$

These are the same as the terms used to work out the PMCC (see p. 28).

③ The gradient (b) of your regression line is given by: $b = \frac{S_{xy}}{S_{xx}}$

④ And the intercept (a) is given by: $a = \bar{y} - b\bar{x}$.

⑤ Then the regression line is just: $y = a + bx$.

Loads of calculators will work out regression lines for you — but you still need to know this method, since they might give you just the sums from Step 1.

Example: Find the equation of the regression line of y on x for the data above.

The 'regression line of y on x' means that x is the independent variable, and y is the dependent variable.

1) Work out the sums: $\sum x = 72.3$, $\sum y = 73.8$, $\sum x^2 = 544.81$, $\sum xy = 511.98$.
2) Then work out S_{xy} and S_{xx}: $S_{xy} = 511.98 - \frac{72.3 \times 73.8}{10} = -21.594$ $S_{xx} = 544.81 - \frac{72.3^2}{10} = 22.081$
3) So the gradient of the regression line is: $b = \frac{-21.594}{22.081} = -0.978$ (to 3 sig. fig.)
4) And the intercept is: $a = \frac{\sum y}{n} - b\frac{\sum x}{n} = \frac{73.8}{10} - (-0.978) \times \frac{72.3}{10} = 14.451$
5) This all means that your regression line is: $y = 14.451 - 0.978x$

Remember: $\bar{x} = \frac{\Sigma x}{n}$

The regression line always goes through the point $(\bar{x}, \bar{y})$.

Regression with ***Coded Data*** is a bit trickier

Examiners can be a bit sneaky so they might ask you to find a regression line for coded data. You could be asked to find the regression line of T on S, say, where $S = x + 15$ and $T = \frac{y}{10}$. Looks confusing, but the method's pretty straightforward. You know that $y = a + bx$ is the regression line for y on x, and you've already found values for a and b above. There's just a couple of extra steps.

1) Find expressions for x and y in terms of S and T. Here $x = S - 15$ and $y = 10T$. Substitute for x and y in $y = a + bx$ to find an expression for T.

$$10T = a + b(S-15) \Rightarrow T = \frac{a-15b}{10} + \frac{b}{10}S$$

2) Now substitute your values for a and b into the expression $T = \frac{a-15b}{10} + \frac{b}{10}S$ to find the regression line of T on S.

Linear Regression

Residuals — the difference between Practice and Theory

A residual is the difference between an observed y-value and the y-value predicted by the regression line.

Residual = Observed y-value – Estimated y-value

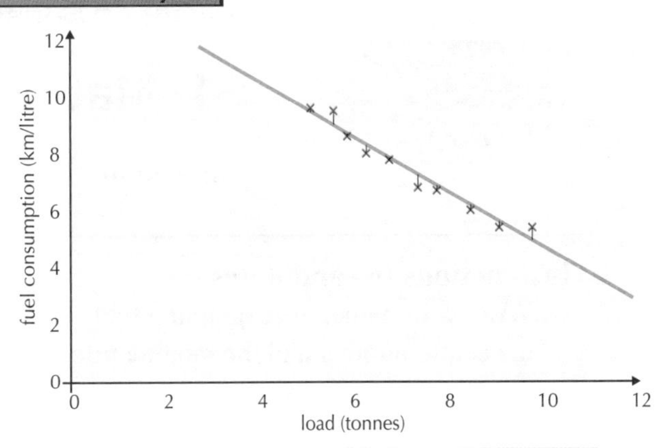

1) Residuals show the experimental error between the y-value that's observed and the y-value your regression line says it should be.
2) Residuals are shown by a vertical line from the actual point to the regression line.

Example: For the fuel consumption example opposite, calculate the residuals for: (i) x = 5.6, (ii) x = 7.4.

(i) When x = 5.6, the residual = 9.5 – (-0.978 × 5.6 + 14.451) = 0.526 (to 3 sig. fig.)
(ii) When x = 7.4, the residual = 6.8 – (-0.978 × 7.4 + 14.451) = -0.414 (to 3 sig. fig.)

A positive residual means the regression line is too low for that value of x.
A negative residual means the regression line is too high.

This kind of regression line is called Least Squares Regression, because you're finding the equation of the line which minimises the sum of the squares of the residuals (i.e. $\sum e_k^2$ is as small as possible, where the e_k are the residuals).

Use Regression Lines With Care

You can use your regression line to predict values of y. But it's best not to do this for x-values outside the range of your original table of values.

Example: Use your regression equation to estimate the value of y when: (i) x = 7.6, (ii) x = 12.6

(i) When x = 7.6, y = –0.978 × 7.6 + 14.451 = 7.02 (to 3 sig. fig.). This should be a pretty reliable guess, since x = 7.6 falls in the range of x we already have readings for — this is called interpolation.

(ii) When x = 12.6, y = –0.978 × 12.6 + 14.451 = 2.13 (to 3 sig. fig.). This may well be unreliable since x = 12.6 is bigger than the biggest x-value we already have — this is called extrapolation.

Practice Question

Sample Exam question:

1. The following times (in seconds) were taken by eight different runners to complete distances of 20 metres and 60 metres.

Runner	A	B	C	D	E	F	G	H
20-metre time (x)	3.39	3.20	3.09	3.32	3.33	3.27	3.44	3.08
60-metre time (y)	8.78	7.73	8.28	8.25	8.91	8.59	8.90	8.05

(a) Plot a scatter diagram to represent the data. [3 marks]
(b) Find the equation of the regression line of y on x and plot it on your scatter diagram. [8 marks]
(c) Use the equation of the regression line to estimate the value of y when: (i) $x = 3.15$, (ii) $x = 3.88$ and comment on the reliability of your estimates. [6 marks]
(d) Find the residuals for: (i) $x = 3.32$, (ii) $x = 3.27$. Illustrate them on your scatter diagram. [4 marks]

99% of all statisticians make sweeping statements...

Be careful with that extrapolation business — it's like me saying that because I grew at an average rate of 10 cm a year for the first few years of my life, by the time I'm 50 I should be 5 metres tall. Residuals are always errors in the values of y — these equations for working out the regression line all assume that you can measure x perfectly all the time.

Exam Board: Edexcel

General Certificate of Education
Advanced Subsidiary (AS) and Advanced Level

S1 Mathematics — Practice Exam

Time allowed: 1 hour 30 minutes.

Instructions to candidates
- Write your name, the examining body (Edexcel), your candidate number, the centre number and the module title in the spaces provided on the answer booklet.
- Answer all questions.

Information for candidates
- The marks available are given in brackets at the end of each question or part-question.
- You may get marks for method, even if your answer is incorrect.
- There are 8 questions in this paper.

Advice to candidates
- Clearly number your answers to parts of questions.
- Don't spend too long on one question.
- If you have time at the end, go back and check your answers.
- You must show enough working to make your method clear. You will gain no marks for answers without working.
- Give non-exact numerical answers correct to 3 significant figures, unless a different degree of accuracy is specified in the question or is clearly appropriate.
- A list of mathematical formulae and statistical tables can be found on page 45.

---

1 A teacher believes there is a linear relationship between the examination mark (M) and the amount of revision undertaken in hours (R). Which of M and R is:

(a) the explanatory variable? *(1 mark)*

(b) the response variable? *(1 mark)*

2 The events A and B are mutually exclusive.
$P(A) = 0.3$ and $P(B) = 0.4$

(a) Write down $P(A \cap B)$. *(1 mark)*

(b) Find $P(A \cup B)$. *(2 marks)*

(c) Hence find the probability that neither event happens. *(2 marks)*

(d) Write down $P(A \mid B)$. Explain your answer. *(2 marks)*

Lea
bla

Leave blank

3 A gambling machine offers cash prizes, x pence, as shown in the probability distribution:

x	0	10	20	50	100
$P(X = x)$	0.2	0.2	0.2	0.2	p

(a) Write down the value of p. *(1 mark)*

(b) State the name of the distribution of X. *(1 mark)*

(c) Find F(25). *(2 marks)*

(d) Find $E(X)$ and $Var(X)$. *(4 marks)*

(e) Find $E(3X - 4)$ and $Var(3X - 4)$. *(4 marks)*

(f) The owner of the machine charges 40p per game. Comment on this cost. *(2 marks)*

(g) Comment on whether the above distribution is really likely to be used in gambling machines. *(2 marks)*

4 A group of 10 friends play a round of golf.

Their total score ($\sum x$) is 500 and $\sum x^2 = 25622$.

(a) Find the mean, μ, and the standard deviation, σ, for this data. *(3 marks)*

(b) Another friend wants to incorporate his score of 50. Without further calculation and giving reasons, explain the effect of adding this score on:

(i) the mean, *(2 marks)*

(ii) the standard deviation. *(2 marks)*

5 The duration in minutes, X, of a car wash is a little erratic, but it is normally distributed with a mean of 8 minutes and a variance of 1.2 minutes. Find:

(a) $P(X < 7.5)$ (to 2 s.f.), *(3 marks)*

(b) the probability that the duration deviates from the mean by more than 1 minute (to 2 s.f.), *(4 marks)*

(c) the duration in minutes, d, such that there is no more than a 1% chance that the car wash will take longer than this duration. *(4 marks)*

Leave blank

6 Of 30 drivers interviewed, 9 have been involved in a car crash at some time. Of those who have been involved in a crash, 5 wear glasses. The probability of wearing glasses, given that the driver has not had a car accident, is $\frac{1}{3}$.

(a) Represent this information in a tree diagram, giving all probabilities as fractions in their simplest form. *(3 marks)*

(b) What is the probability that a person chosen at random wears glasses? *(3 marks)*

(c) What is the probability that a glasses wearer has been a crash victim? *(3 marks)*

7 A box of chocolates contains 20 chocolates, all of which are either hard or soft centred. Some of the chocolates contain nuts. 13 chocolates have hard centres, of which 6 contain nuts. There are 10 nutty chocolates in total.

(a) Represent the data in a Venn diagram. *(2 marks)*

(b) A chocolate is selected at random. Find the probability of:

(i) it having a soft centre. *(1 mark)*

(ii) it having a hard centre, given that it contains a nut. *(3 marks)*

(c) If 3 chocolates are selected at random without replacement, find the probability that exactly one has a hard centre. *(3 marks)*

8 The discrete random variable X has the probability distribution function shown below:

$$P(X = x) = \begin{cases} \dfrac{kx}{6} & \text{for } x = 1, 2, 3 \\ \dfrac{k(7-x)}{6} & \text{for } x = 4, 5, 6 \\ 0 & \text{otherwise} \end{cases}$$

(a) Find the value of k. *(3 marks)*

(b) Find F(3). *(2 marks)*

(c) Show that $E(X) = 3.5$. *(2 marks)*

(d) Given that $\text{Var}(X) = \frac{23}{12}$ find (to 2 d.p.):

(i) $E(2 - 3X)$ and $\text{Var}(2 - 3X)$, *(4 marks)*

(ii) $E(X^2)$. *(3 marks)*

Answers

Section One — Data

Page 3

1) 12.8, 13.2, 13.5, 14.3, 14.3, 14.6, 14.8, 15.2, 15.9, 16.1, 16.1, 16.2, 16.3, 17.0, 17.2 (all in cm)

2)

Boys		Girls
9, 5	1	2
7, 6, 2, 0	2	1, 4, 5, 7, 8, 9
9, 7, 4, 2	3	1, 6, 7, 8, 9

Key 2|1|3 means: Boys 12, Girls 13

3)

Length of call	Lower class boundary (lcb)	Upper class boundary (ucb)	Class width	Frequency	Frequency density = Height of column
0 - 2	0	2.5	2.5	10	4
3 - 5	2.5	5.5	3	6	2
6 - 8	5.5	8.5	3	3	1
9 - 15	8.5	15.5	7	1	0.143

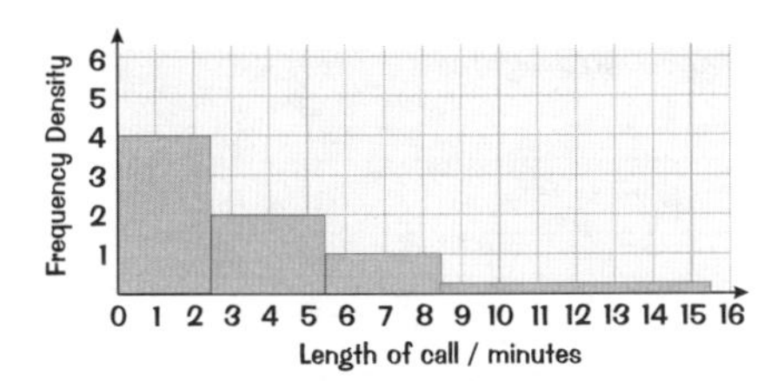

4) a)

Profit	Class width	Frequency	Frequency density = Height of column
4.5 - 5.0	0.5	24	48
5.0 - 5.5	0.5	26	52
5.5 - 6.0	0.5	21	42
6.0 - 6.5	0.5	19	38
6.5 - 8.0	1.5	10	6.67

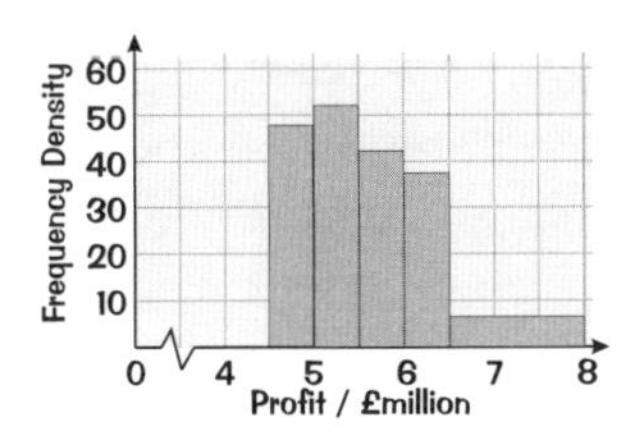

[1 mark for correct axes, then up to 2 marks for the bars drawn correctly]

b) *The distribution is positively skewed — only a few businesses make a high profit. The modal profit is between £5 million and £5.5 million.*
[Up to 2 marks available for any sensible comments]

Page 5

1) *$\Sigma f = 16$, $\Sigma fx = 22$, so mean = 22 ÷ 16 = 1.375*
Median position = 17 ÷ 2 = 8.5, so median = 1
Mode = 0.

2)

Speed	mid-class value x	Number of cars f	fx
30 - 34	32	12 (12)	384
35 - 39	37	37 (49)	1369
40 - 44	42	9	378
45 - 50	47.5	2	95
	Totals	60	2226

Estimated mean = 2226 ÷ 60 = 37.1 mph
Median position is 61 ÷ 2 = 30.5.
This is in class 35 - 39.
30.5 – 12 = 18.5, so median is 18.5th value in class.
Class width = 5, so median is:

$$34.5 + \left(18 \times \frac{5}{37}\right) = 36.9 \text{ mph}$$

Modal class is 35 - 39 mph.

3) a) *There are 30 males, so median is in 31 ÷ 2 = 15.5th position. Take the mean of the 15th and 16th readings to get median = (62 + 65) ÷ 2 = 63.5 [1 mark]*

b) *The female median is 64.5 (halfway between the 8th and 9th readings). Female median is higher than the male median. The females scored better than the males on average.*
Female range = 79 – 55 = 24.
Male range = 79 – 43 = 36
The female range is less than the male range. Their scores are more consistent than the males'.
[Up to 2 marks available for any sensible comments]

Page 7

1)

Distance	Upper class boundary (ucb)	f	Cumulative frequency (cf)
	0	0	0
0 - 2	2	10	10
2 - 4	4	5	15
4 - 6	6	3	18
6 - 8	8	2	20

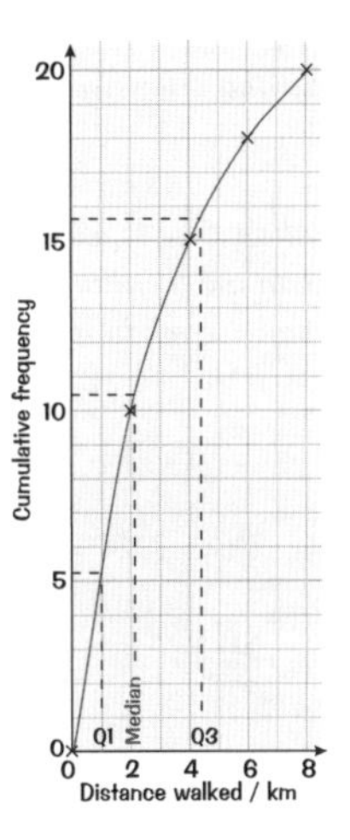

Median = 2.2 km (approximately)
Q_1 = 1 km, Q_3 = 4.4 km,
so interquartile range = 3.4 km (approximately)

2) a)

Age	Upper class boundary (ucb)	f	Cumulative frequency (cf)
Under 5	5	0	0
5 - 10	11	2	2
11 - 15	16	3	5
16 - 20	21	10	15
21 - 30	31	2	17
31 - 40	41	2	19
41 - 70	71	1	20

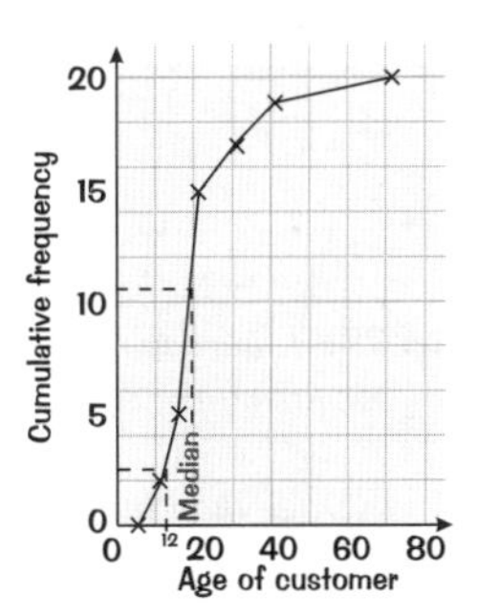

[1 mark for correctly labelled axes, up to 2 marks for calculating the points and plotting them correctly, and 1 mark for joining the points with straight lines or a suitable curve]

b) (i) *Median = 18.5 years (approximately) [1 mark]*
(ii) *Number of customers under 12 = 2 (approximately) [1 mark]*
So number of customers over 12 = 20 – 2 = 18 (approximately) [1 mark]

3) a) (i) *Times = 2, 3, 4, 4, 5, 5, 5, 7, 10, 12*
Median position = 5.5, so median = 5 minutes [1 mark]
(ii) *Lower quartile = 4 minutes [1 mark]*
Upper quartile = 7 minutes [1 mark]

Answers

b) 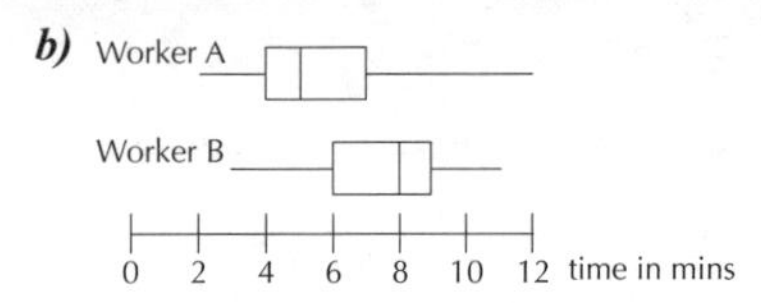

[Up to 3 marks available for each graph — get 1 mark for the median in the right place, 1 mark for both of the quartiles shown correctly, and 1 mark for the lines showing the extremes drawn correctly]

c) *Various statements could be made, e.g. the times for Worker B are longer than those for Worker A, on average.*
The IQR for both workers is the same — generally they both work with the same consistency.
The range for Worker A is larger than that for Worker B. Worker A has a few items he/she can iron very quickly and a few which take a long time.
[1 mark for any sensible answer]

d) *Worker A would be best to employ. The median time is less than for Worker B, and the Upper Quartile is less than the median of Worker B. Worker A would generally iron more items in a given time than worker B.*
[1 mark for any sensible answer]

Page 9

1) $$\text{Mean} = \frac{11+12+14+17+21+23+27}{7} = \frac{125}{7} = 17.9 \text{ to 3 sig. fig.}$$

$$\text{s.d.} = \sqrt{\frac{11^2+12^2+14^2+17^2+21^2+23^2+27^2}{7} - \left(\frac{125}{7}\right)^2} = \sqrt{30.98} = 5.57 \text{ to 3 sig. fig.}$$

2)

Score	Mid-class value, x	x^2	f	fx	fx^2
100 - 106	103	10609	6	618	63654
107 - 113	110	12100	11	1210	133100
114 - 120	117	13689	22	2574	301158
121 - 127	124	15376	9	1116	138384
128 - 134	131	17161	2	262	34322
		Totals	50 (= Σf)	5780 (= Σfx)	670618 (= Σfx^2)

$$\text{Mean} = \frac{5780}{50} = 115.6$$

$$s^2 = \frac{670618}{50} - 115.6^2 = 49$$

So $s = 7$

3) a) $\bar{A} = \frac{60.3}{20} = 3.015\text{ g}$ *[1 mark]*

b) $s_A^2 = \frac{219}{20} - 3.015^2 = 1.86\text{ g}^2$

So $s_A = 1.36$ g to 3 sig. fig.

[3 marks for the correct answer — otherwise 1 mark for a correct method to find the variance, and 1 mark for taking the square root to find the s.d.]

c) *Brand A chocolate drops are heavier on average than brand B. Brand B chocolate drops are much closer to the mean of 2.95 g.*
[1 mark for each of 2 sensible statements]

d) $$\text{Mean of } A \text{ and } B = \frac{\sum A + \sum B}{50} = \frac{60.3 + (30 \times 2.95)}{50} = 2.976\text{ g}$$

$$\frac{\sum B^2}{30} - 2.95^2 = 1, \text{ and so } \sum B^2 = 291.075$$

$$\text{Variance of } A \text{ and } B = \frac{\sum A^2 + \sum B^2}{50} - 2.976^2 = \frac{219 + 291.075}{50} - 2.976^2$$

$= 1.3449$

So s.d. $= \sqrt{1.3449} = 1.16$ g to 3 sig. fig

[4 marks for the correct answer — otherwise 1 mark for the correct total mean, 1 mark for the sum of the B^2, 1 mark for the correct method to find the total variance/standard deviation]

Page 11

1) Let $y = x - 20$.

Then $\bar{y} = \bar{x} - 20$ or $\bar{x} = \bar{y} + 20$

$\sum y = 125$ and $\sum y^2 = 221$

So $\bar{y} = \frac{125}{100} = 1.25$ and $\bar{x} = 1.25 + 20 = \underline{21.25}$

$s_y^2 = \frac{221}{100} - 1.25^2 = 0.6475$ and so $s_y = 0.805$ to 3 sig. fig.

Therefore $s_x = 0.805$ to 3 sig. fig.

2)

Time	Mid-class x	$y = x - 35.5$	f	fy	fy^2
30 - 33	31.5	-4	3	-12	48
34 - 37	35.5	0	6	0	0
38 - 41	39.5	4	7	28	112
42 - 45	43.5	8	4	32	256
		Totals	20 (= Σf)	48 (= Σfy)	416 (= Σfy^2)

$\bar{y} = \frac{48}{20} = 2.4$

So $\bar{x} = \bar{y} + 35.5 = 2.4 + 35.5 = \underline{37.9 \text{ minutes}}$

$s_y^2 = \frac{416}{20} - 2.4^2 = 15.04$, and so $s_y = 3.88$ minutes, to 3 sig. fig.

But $s_x = s_y$, and so $\underline{s_x = 3.88 \text{ minutes}}$, to 3 sig. fig.

3) a) Let $y = x - 30$.

$\bar{y} = \frac{228}{19} = 12$ and so $\underline{\bar{x} = \bar{y} + 30 = 42}$

$s_y^2 = \frac{3040}{19} - 12^2 = 16$ and so $s_y = 4$

But $s_x = s_y$ and so $\underline{s_x = 4}$

[3 marks for the correct answers — otherwise 1 mark for the correct mean and 1 mark for the correct s.d. or variance of y]

b) $\bar{x} = \frac{\sum x}{19} = 42$

And so $\sum x = 42 \times 19 = \underline{798}$

$s_x^2 = \frac{\sum x^2}{19} - \bar{x}^2 = \frac{\sum x^2}{19} - 42^2 = 16$

And so $\sum x^2 = (16 + 42^2) \times 19 = \underline{33820}$

[3 marks for both correct answers — otherwise 1 mark for either correct]

c) New $\sum x = 798 + 32 = 830$.

So new $\bar{x} = \frac{830}{20} = \underline{41.5}$

New $\sum x^2 = 33820 + 32^2 = 34844$.

So new $s_x^2 = \frac{34844}{20} - 41.5^2 = 19.95$ and new $\underline{s_x = 4.47}$ to 3 sig. fig.

[2 marks for each correct answer — otherwise 1 mark for some correct working for each part]

Page 13

1) *IQR = 88 – 62 = 26, so 3 × IQR = 78.*
So upper fence = 88 + 78 = 166.
This means that: ***a)*** *161 is not an outlier.* ***b)*** *176 is an outlier.*
Lower fence = 62 – 78 = -16.
This means that: ***c)*** *0 is not an outlier.*

Answers

2) *Put the 20 items of data in order:*
1, 4, 5, 5, 5, 5, 5, 6, 6, 7, 7, 8, 10, 10, 12, 15, 20, 20, 30, 50
Then the median position is 10.5, and since the 10th and the 11th items are both 7, the median = 7.
Lower quartile = 5.
Upper quartile = (12 + 15) ÷ 2 = 13.5.

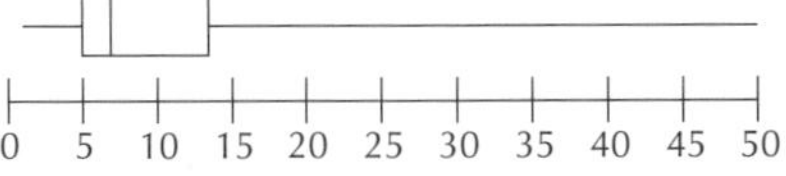

This data is positively skewed. Most 15-year-olds earned a small amount of pocket money. A few got very large amounts.

3) *Pearson's coefficient of skewness* $= \frac{10.3 - 10}{1.5} = 0.2$

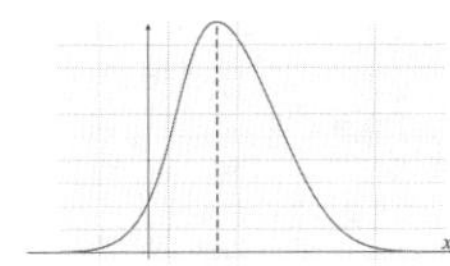

— possible shape

This is positively skewed, but not by much.

4) a) *Total number of people = 38.*
Median position = (38 + 1) ÷ 2 = 19.5.
19th value = 15; 20th value = 16, so median = 15.5 hits.
Mode = 15 hits.
[2 marks for the correct median, otherwise 1 mark for some correct working, plus 1 mark for the correct mode]

b) *Lower quartile = 10th value = 14*
Upper quartile = 29th value = 17. [1 mark for both]
So interquartile range = 17 – 14 = 3,
and upper fence = 17 + (3 × 3) = 26.
This means that 25 is not an outlier. [1 mark]

c)

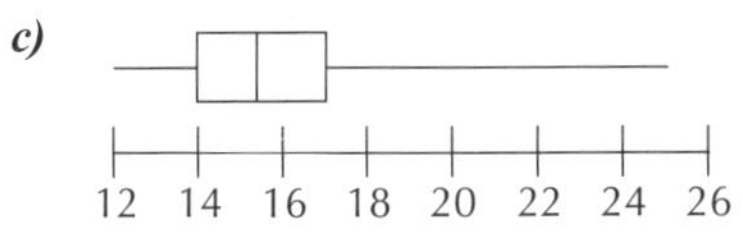

[1 mark]
The distribution is positively skewed. [1 mark]
(Different kinds of sketch would be allowed.)

d) *If 25 was removed then the right-hand tail of the box plot would be much shorter, and the distribution would be less positively skewed. [1 mark]*

5) a)

mm of rain	Upper class boundary (ucb)	f	Cumulative frequency (cf)
Under 5	5	0	0
5 - 10	10	2	2
10 - 15	15	3	5
15 - 20	20	5	10
20 - 25	25	7	17
25 - 30	30	10	27
30 - 35	35	3	30

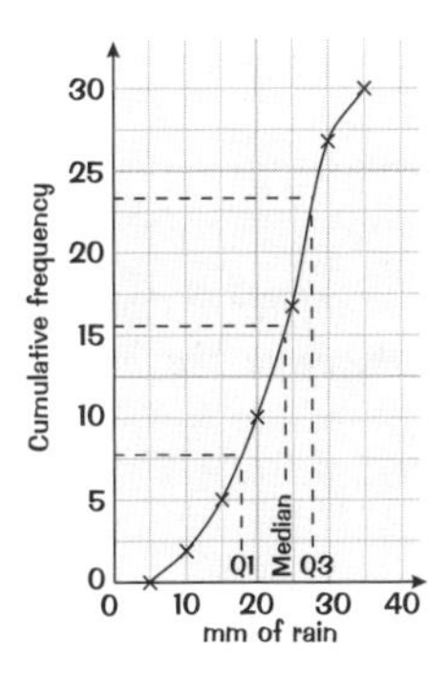

[Up to 2 marks for correctly calculating and plotting the points, plus 1 mark for correct axes/labels etc.]

b) *From the diagram, median = 24. [1 mark for answer in range 23.5-24.5]*
Lower quartile = 17.5. [1 mark for answer in the range 17-18]
Upper quartile = 27.5. [1 mark for answer in the range 27-28]

c) *Quartile coefficient of skewness* $= \frac{27.5 - (2 \times 24) + 17.5}{27.5 - 17.5} = -0.3$
[1 mark — answers may differ slightly, depending on answers to part b)]
The graph is negatively skewed — most of the days tend to have higher rainfall. [1 mark]

Section Two — Probability

Page 15

1) a) *The sample space would be as below:*

Coin	Dice 1	2	3	4	5	6
H	2	4	6	8	10	12
T	5	6	7	8	9	10

b) *There are 12 outcomes in total, and 9 of these are more than 5, so P(score >5) = 9/12 = 3/4*

c) *There are 6 outcomes which have a tail showing, and 3 of these are even, so P(even score given that you throw a tail) = 3/6 = 1/2*

2) a) *20% of the people eat chips, and 10% of these is 2% — so 2% eat both chips and sausages.*
Now you can draw the Venn diagram:

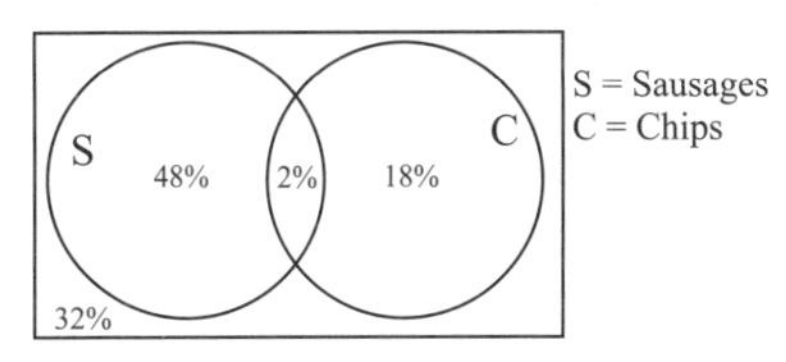

By reading the numbers in the appropriate sets from the diagram you can see

b) *18% eat chips but not sausages.*

c) *18% + 48% = 66% eat chips or sausages, but not both.*

3) a) *The Venn diagram would look something like this:*

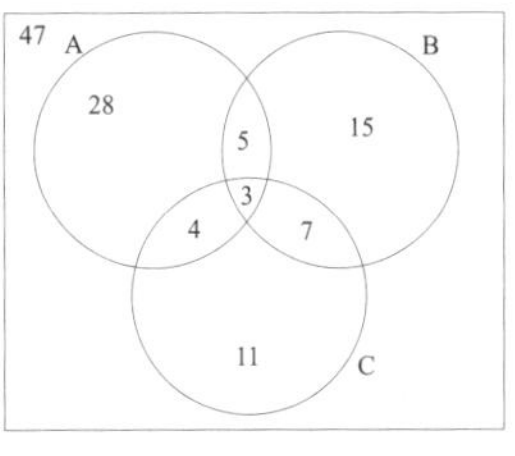

[1 mark for the central figure correct, 2 marks for '5', '7' and '4' correct (get 1 mark for 2 correct), plus 2 marks for '28', '15' and '11' correct (get 1 mark for 2 correct)]

b) (i) *Add up the numbers in all the circles to get 73 people out of 120 buy at least 1 type of soap. So the probability = 73/120 [2 marks]*

(ii) *Add up the numbers in the intersections to get 5 + 3 + 4 + 7 = 19, meaning that 19 people buy at least two soaps, so the probability a person buys at least two types = 19/120 [2 marks]*

(iii) *28 + 11 + 15 = 54 people buy only 1 soap, and of these 15 buy soap B [1 mark]. So probability of a person who only buys one type of soap buying type B is 15/54 = 5/18 [2 marks]*

Answers

Page 17

1) *Draw a sample space diagram*

2nd Dice						
6	7	8	9	10	11	12
5	6	7	8	9	10	11
4	5	6	7	8	9	10
3	4	5	6	7	8	9
2	3	4	5	6	7	8
1	2	3	4	5	6	7
	1	2	3	4	5	6

1st Dice

There are 36 outcomes altogether.

a) *15 outcomes are prime (since 2, 3, 5, 7 and 11 are prime), so P(prime) = 15/36 = 5/12*

b) *7 outcomes are square numbers (4 and 9), so P(square) = 7/36*

c) *Being prime and a square number are exclusive events, so P(prime or square) = 15/36 + 7/36 = 22/36 = 11/18*

2) a)

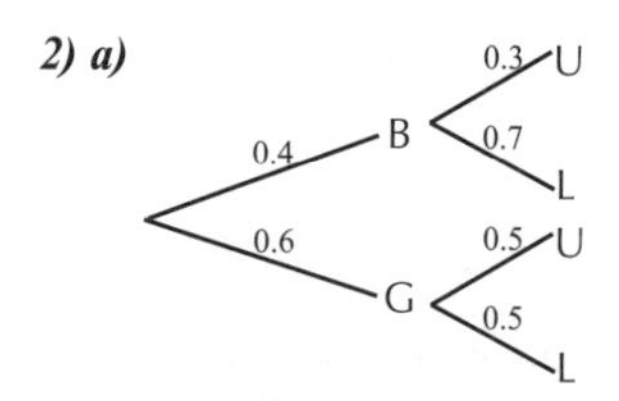

b) *Choosing an upper school pupil means either 'boy and upper' or 'girl and upper'. P(boy and upper) = 0.4 × 0.3 = 0.12. P(girl and upper) = 0.6 × 0.5 = 0.30. So P(Upper) = 0.12 + 0.30 = 0.42.*

3) a)

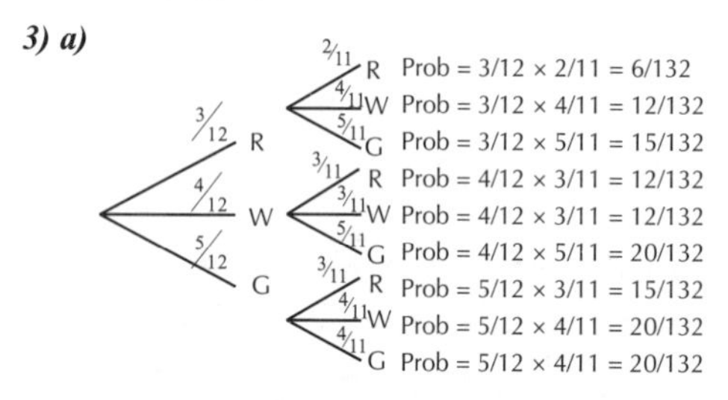

[3 marks available — 1 mark for each set of 3 branches on the right-hand side correct]

b) *The second counter is green means one of three outcomes 'red then green'* ***or*** *'white then green'* ***or*** *'green then green'. So Prob(2nd is green) = 15/132 + 20/32 + 20/132 = 55/132 = 5/12 [2 marks]*

c) *For both to be red there's only one outcome: 'red then red' Prob(both red) = 6/132 = 1/22 [2 marks]*

d) *'Both same colour' is the complementary event of 'not both same colour'.*
So Prob (not same colour) = 1 – P(both same colour)
Both same colour is either R and R or W and W or G and G
Prob(not same colour) = 1 – [6/132 + 12/132 + 20/132]
= 1 – 38/132 =94/132 = 47/66
[3 marks for the correct answer — otherwise up to 2 marks available for using a suitable method]

Page 19

1) *You could draw a Venn diagram — but you don't have to, it just makes things easier.*

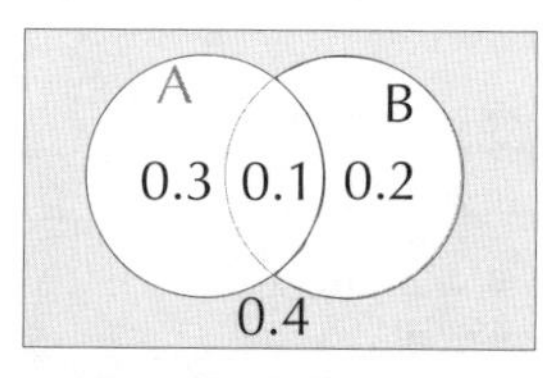

a) *P(B|A) = P(A∩B)÷ P(A) = 0.1÷0.4 = 0.25*

b) *P(B|A') = P(A'∩B)÷P(A') = 0.2÷0.6 = 1/3*

c) *P(B|A) = 0.25, but P(B) = 0.3 so they're not independent.*

2) *Draw a tree diagram:*

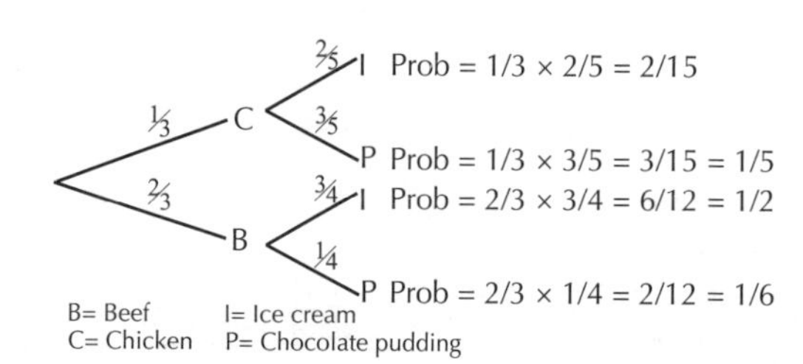

a) *P(chicken or ice cream but not both) = P(C∩P) + P(B∩I) = 1/5 + 1/2 = 7/10*

b) *P(ice cream) = P(C∩I) + P(B∩I) = 2/15 + 1/2 = 19/30*

c) *P(chicken|ice cream) = P(C∩I) ÷ P(I)= (2/15) ÷ (19/30) = 4/19*

3) a) (i) *V and W are independent, so P(V ∩ W) = P(V) × P(W) = 0.2 × 0.6 = 0.12 [1 mark]*

(ii) *P(V ∪ W) = P(V) + P(W) – P(V ∩ W) = 0.2 + 0.6 – 0.12 = 0.68 [2 marks]*

b) *Drawing a quick Venn Diagram often helps:*

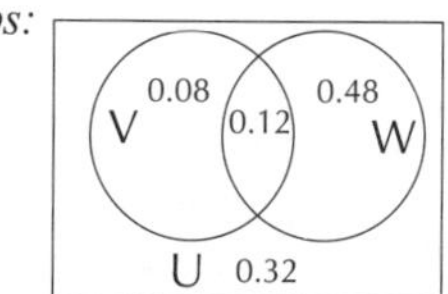

P(U|V') = P(U ∩ V') ÷ P(V')
Now U ∩ V' = U — think about it — all of U is contained in V', so U ∩ V' (the 'bits in both U and V') are just the bits in U.
Therefore P(U ∩ V') = P(U) = 1 – P(V ∪ W) = 1 – 0.68 = 0.32
P(V') = 1 – P(V) = 1 – 0.2 = 0.8
And so P(U|V') = 0.32 ÷ 0.8 = 0.4
[3 marks for the correct answer — otherwise up to 2 marks available for correct working]

4) *Draw a tree diagram*

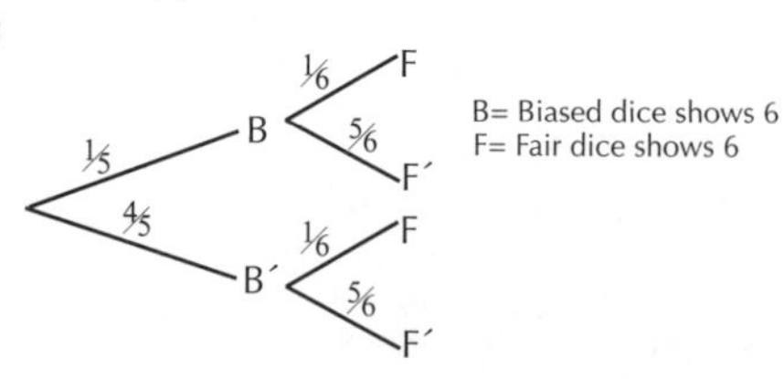

a) *P(B') = 0.8 [1 mark]*

b) *Either at least one of the dice shows a 6 or neither of them do, so these are complementary events. Call F the event 'the fair dice shows a 6'.*
Then P(F ∪ B) = 1 – P(F' ∩ B') = 1 – (4/5 × 5/6) = 1 – 2/3 = 1/3 [2 marks]

Answers

c) *P(exactly one 6 | at least one 6)*
= P(exactly one 6 ∩ at least one 6) ÷ P(at least one 6).
This next step might be a bit easier to get your head round if you draw a Venn diagram.

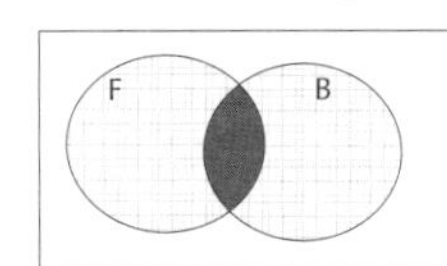

'exactly one 6' ∩ 'at least one 6' = 'exactly one 6'
(Look at the diagram — 'exactly one 6' is the cross-hatched area, and 'at least one 6' is the cross-hatched area plus the grey bit. So the bit in common to both is just the cross-hatched area.)
Now, that means P(exactly one 6 ∩ at least one 6) = P(B∩F') + P(B'∩F) — this is the cross-hatched area in the Venn diagram, i.e. P(exactly one 6 ∩ at least one 6) = (1/5 × 5/6) + (4/5 × 1/6) = 9/30 = 3/10 (using the fact that B and F are independent).
P(at least one 6) = 1/5 + 1/6 – (1/5 × 1/6) = 10/30 = 1/3
And all of this means P(exactly one 6 | at least one 6) = 3/10 ÷ 1/3 = 9/10
[3 marks for the correct answer — otherwise up to 2 marks available for correct working]

Section Three — Probability Distributions

Page 21

1) a) *All the probabilities have to add up to 1.*
So 0.5 + k + k + 3k = 0.5 + 5k = 1, i.e. 5k = 0.5, i.e. k = 0.1.

b) *P(Y < 2) = P(Y = 0) + P(Y = 1) = 0.5 + 0.1 = 0.6.*

2) *Make a table showing the possible values of X, i.e. total scores on the dice (though there are other ways to do this):*

Score on dice 1 (columns), Score on dice 2 (rows)

+	1	1	1	2	2	3
1	2	2	2	3	3	4
1	2	2	2	3	3	4
1	2	2	2	3	3	4
2	3	3	3	4	4	5
2	3	3	3	4	4	5
3	4	4	4	5	5	6

There are 36 outcomes in total, and of these 10 have X = 4.

So $P(X = 4) = \frac{10}{36} = \frac{5}{18}$.

Altogether there are 5 possible values for X, and the rest of the pdf is found in the same way that you found P(X = 4). The pdf is summarised in this table:

x	2	3	4	5	6
P(X = x)	1/4	1/3	5/18	1/9	1/36

3) a) *The probability of getting 3 heads is:* $\frac{1}{2}\times\frac{1}{2}\times\frac{1}{2}=\frac{1}{8}$ *[1 mark]*

The probability of getting 2 heads is: $3\times\frac{1}{2}\times\frac{1}{2}\times\frac{1}{2}=\frac{3}{8}$ *(multiply by 3 because any of the three coins could be the tail — the order in which the heads and the tail occur isn't important). [1 mark]*

Similarly the probability of getting 1 head is: $3\times\frac{1}{2}\times\frac{1}{2}\times\frac{1}{2}=\frac{3}{8}$.
[1 mark]

And the probability of getting no heads is $\frac{1}{2}\times\frac{1}{2}\times\frac{1}{2}=\frac{1}{8}$. *[1 mark]*

Hence the pdf of X is:

x	20p	10p	*nothing*
P(X = x)	1/8	3/8	1/2

b) *You need the probability that X >10p [1 mark]. This is just*
P(X = 20p) = $\frac{1}{8}$ *[1 mark]*

Page 23

1) $P(W \le 0.2) = P(W = 0.2) = 0.2$

$P(W \le 0.3) = P(W = 0.2) + P(W = 0.3) = 0.4$

$P(W \le 0.4) = P(W = 0.2) + P(W = 0.3) + P(W = 0.4) = 0.7$

$P(W \le 0.5) = P(W = 0.2) + P(W = 0.3) + P(W = 0.4) + P(W = 0.5) = 1$

So the cumulative distribution function of W is:

w	0.2	0.3	0.4	0.5
P(W ≤ w)	0.2	0.4	0.7	1

2) $P(R=0) = P(R \le 0) = F(0) = 0.1$

$P(R=1) = P(R \le 1) - P(R \le 0) = 0.5 - 0.1 = 0.4$

$P(R=2) = P(R \le 2) - P(R \le 1) = 1 - 0.5 = 0.5$

So the pdf of R is:

r	0	1	2
P(R = r)	0.1	0.4	0.5

$P(0 \le R \le 1) = 0.5$

3) *There are 5 possible outcomes, and the probability of each of them is k, so k = 1 ÷ 5 = 0.2.*

Mean of X = $\frac{0+4}{2} = 2$.

Variance of X = $\frac{(4-0+1)^2-1}{12} = \frac{24}{12} = 2$.

4) a) *All the probabilities must add up to 1, so 2k + 3k + k + k = 1, i.e. 7k = 1, and so* $k = \frac{1}{7}$. *[1 mark]*

b) $P(X \le 0) = P(X = 0) = \frac{2}{7}$ *[1 mark]*

$P(X \le 1) = P(X = 0) + P(X = 1) = \frac{5}{7}$ *[1 mark]*

$P(X \le 2) = P(X = 0) + P(X = 1) + P(X = 2) = \frac{6}{7}$ *[1 mark]*

$P(X \le 3) = P(X = 0) + P(X = 1) + P(X = 2) + P(X = 3) = 1$ *[1 mark]*

So the distribution function is as in the following table:

x	0	1	2	3
P(X ≤ x)	2/7	5/7	6/7	1

c) $P(X > 2) = 1 - P(X \le 2) = 1 - \frac{6}{7} = \frac{1}{7}$ *[1 mark]*
(Or P(X > 2) = P(X = 3) = $\frac{1}{7}$*, using part a).)*

5) a)

x	0	1	2	3	4	5	6	7	8	9
P(X = x)	0.1	0.1	0.1	0.1	0.1	0.1	0.1	0.1	0.1	0.1

[1 mark]

b) $Mean = \frac{0+9}{2} = 4.5$ *[1 mark]* $Variance = \frac{(9-0+1)^2-1}{12} = \frac{99}{12} = 8.25$
[2 marks]

c) $P(X < 4.5) = P(X=0) + P(X=1) + P(X=2) + P(X=3) + P(X=4) = 0.5$
[2 marks]

Page 25

1) a) *As always, the probabilities have to add up to 1, so*

$k = 1 - \left(\frac{1}{6} + \frac{1}{2} + \frac{5}{24}\right) = 1 - \frac{21}{24} = \frac{3}{24} = \frac{1}{8}$

b) $E(X) = \left(1\times\frac{1}{6}\right) + \left(2\times\frac{1}{2}\right) + \left(3\times\frac{1}{8}\right) + \left(4\times\frac{5}{24}\right) = \frac{4+24+9+20}{24} = \frac{57}{24} = \frac{19}{8}$

$E(X^2) = \left(1^1\times\frac{1}{6}\right) + \left(2^2\times\frac{1}{2}\right) + \left(3^2\times\frac{1}{8}\right) + \left(4^2\times\frac{5}{24}\right) = \frac{4+48+27+80}{24} = \frac{159}{24}$

$Var(X) = E(X^2) - [E(X)]^2 = \frac{159}{24} - \left(\frac{57}{24}\right)^2 = \frac{3816-3249}{576} = \frac{567}{576} = \frac{63}{64}$

Answers

c) $E(2X-1)=2E(X)-1=2\times\frac{19}{8}-1=\frac{30}{8}=\frac{15}{4}$

$Var(2X-1)=2^2Var(X)=4\times\frac{63}{64}=\frac{63}{16}$

2) a) *P(X = 1) = a, P(X = 2) = 2a, P(X = 3) = 3a. Therefore the total probability is 3a + 2a + a = 6a. This must equal 1, so* $a=\frac{1}{6}$. *[1 mark]*

b) $E(X)=\left(1\times\frac{1}{6}\right)+\left(2\times\frac{2}{6}\right)+\left(3\times\frac{3}{6}\right)=\frac{1+4+9}{6}=\frac{14}{6}=\frac{7}{3}$ *[2 marks]*

c) $E(X^2)=Var(X)+\left[E(X)\right]^2=\frac{5}{9}+\left(\frac{7}{3}\right)^2=\frac{5+49}{9}=\frac{54}{9}=6$ *[2 marks]*

d) $E(3X+4)=3E(X)+4=3\times\frac{7}{3}+4=11$ *[1 mark]*

$Var(3X+4)=3^2Var(X)=9\times\frac{5}{9}=5$ *[2 marks]*

Page 27

1) a) *Normalise the probabilities and then use tables to answer these. Remember, X ~ N(50, 16) (and 16 is the variance, not the standard deviation).*

$P(X<55)=P\left(Z<\frac{55-50}{\sqrt{16}}\right)=P(Z<1.25)=0.8944$

b) $P(X<42)=P\left(Z<\frac{42-50}{\sqrt{16}}\right)=P(Z<-2)$

$=1-P(Z<2)=1-0.9772=0.0228$

c) $P(X>56)=1-P(X<56)=1-P\left(Z<\frac{56-50}{\sqrt{16}}\right)=$

$1-P(Z<1.5)=1-0.9332=0.0668$

d) $P(47<X<57)=P(X<57)-P(X<47)=P\left(Z<\frac{57-50}{\sqrt{16}}\right)-P\left(Z<\frac{47-50}{\sqrt{16}}\right)$

$=P(Z<1.75)-P(Z<-0.75)$

$=P(Z<1.75)-(1-P(Z<0.75))$

$=0.9599-(1-0.7734)$

$=0.7333$

2) a) *Here X ~ N(600, 202). You need to use your 'percentage points' table for these.*

If $P(X<a)=0.95$*, then* $P\left(Z<\frac{a-600}{\sqrt{202}}\right)=0.95$.

So $\frac{a-600}{\sqrt{202}}=1.645$ *(using the table).*

Rearrange this to get $a=600+1.645\times\sqrt{202}=623.38$

b) *|X – 600| < b means that X is 'within b' of 600, i.e. 600 – b < X < 600 + b. Since 600 is the mean of X, and since a normal distribution is symmetrical,*

$P(600-b<X<600+b)=0.8$ *means that* $P(600<X<600+b)=0.4$

i.e. $P\left(\frac{600-600}{\sqrt{202}}<Z<\frac{600+b-600}{\sqrt{202}}\right)=0.4$, *i.e.* $P\left(0<Z<\frac{b}{\sqrt{202}}\right)=0.4$

This means that $P\left(Z<\frac{b}{\sqrt{202}}\right)-P(Z<0)=0.4$

i.e. $P\left(Z<\frac{b}{\sqrt{202}}\right)-0.5=0.4$, *or* $P\left(Z<\frac{b}{\sqrt{202}}\right)=0.9$

Use your percentage points table to find that

$\frac{b}{\sqrt{202}}=1.2816$, *or* $b=1.2816\times\sqrt{202}=18.21$

3 a) *Here, the random variable X (the distribution of the marks) is distributed X ~ N(50, 30²). First, you need P(X > 41) — this will tell you the fraction of marks that are above 41.*

$P(X>41)=P\left(Z>\frac{41-50}{30}\right)=P(Z>-0.3)$

This is equal to $P(Z<0.3)=0.6179$ *(from tables). [2 marks]*

Then to estimate the number of candidates that passed the exam, multiply this by 1000 — so roughly 618 students are likely to have passed [1 mark].

b) *Let the mark required for an A-grade be k. Then since 90% of students don't get an A, P(X < k) = 0.9 [1 mark]*

Normalise this to get $P\left[Z<\frac{k-50}{30}\right]=0.9$ *[1 mark]*

Now you can use your percentage points table to get that

$\frac{k-50}{30}=1.282$*, or* $k=30\times1.282+50=88.46$ *[1 mark]. So the mark needed for an A-grade will be around 88-89 marks.*

4) *Assume that the lives of the batteries are distributed as* $N(\mu,\sigma^2)$. *Then P(X < 20) = 0.4 [1 mark] and P(X < 30) = 0.8. Normalise these 2 equations to get*

$P\left[Z<\frac{20-\mu}{\sigma}\right]=0.4$ *and* $P\left[Z<\frac{30-\mu}{\sigma}\right]=0.8$ *[1 mark]*

Now you need to use your percentage points table to get:

$\frac{20-\mu}{\sigma}=-0.2533$ *and* $\frac{30-\mu}{\sigma}=0.8416$ *[2 marks]*

Now rewrite these as:

$20-\mu=-0.2533\sigma$ *and* $30-\mu=0.8416\sigma$. *[1 mark]*

Subtract these two equations to get:

$10=(0.8416+0.2533)\sigma$

i.e. $\sigma=\frac{10}{0.8416+0.2533}=9.1333$ *[1 mark]*

Now use this value of σ in one of the equations above:

$\mu=20+0.2533\times9.1333=22.31$ *[1 mark]*

So $X\sim N(22.31,\ 9.13^2)$ *i.e.* $X\sim N(22.31, 83.4)$

Section Four — Correlation and Regression

Page 29

1)

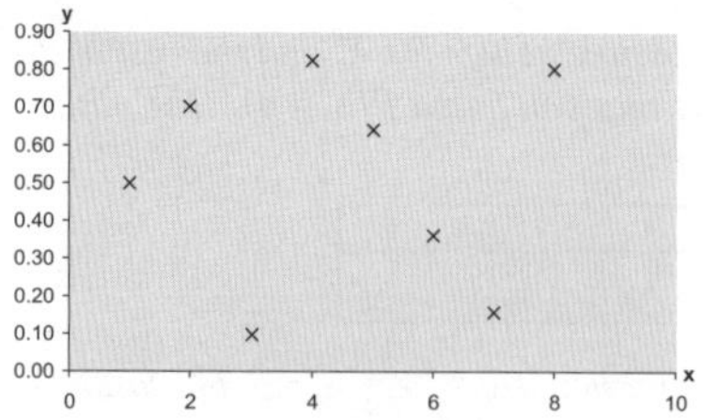

[Up to 2 marks available]

You need to work out these sums:

$\sum x=36$, $\sum y=4.08$, $\sum x^2=204$, $\sum y^2=2.6272$, $\sum xy=18.36$.

[5 marks available — 1 for each correct sum]

Then $r=\frac{18.36-\frac{36\times4.08}{8}}{\sqrt{\left[204-\frac{36^2}{8}\right]\left[2.6272-\frac{4.08^2}{8}\right]}}=\frac{0}{\sqrt{42\times0.5464}}=0$ *[1 mark]*

This value of zero for the correlation tells you that there appears to be no linear relationship between the two variables [1 mark].

Answers

Page 31

1) a)

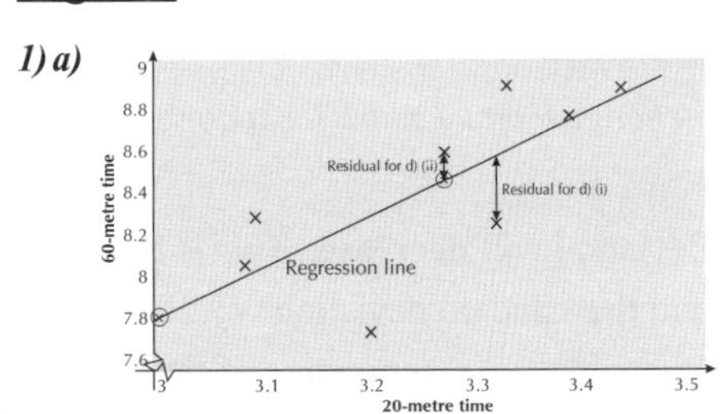

[3 marks available for the scatter diagram]

b) *It's best to make a table like this one, first:*

									Totals
20-metre time, x	3.39	3.2	3.09	3.32	3.33	3.27	3.44	3.08	26.12
60-metre time, y	8.78	7.73	8.28	8.25	8.91	8.59	8.9	8.05	67.49
x^2	11.4921	10.24	9.5481	11.0224	11.0889	10.6929	11.8336	9.4864	85.4044
xy	29.7642	24.736	25.5852	27.39	29.6703	28.0893	30.616	24.794	220.645

[2 marks available for at least 3 correct totals on the right-hand side]

Then: $S_{xy} = 220.645 - \dfrac{26.12 \times 67.49}{8} = 0.29015$ *[1 mark]*

$S_{xx} = 85.4044 - \dfrac{26.12^2}{8} = 0.1226$ *[1 mark]*

Then the gradient b is given by: $b = \dfrac{S_{xy}}{S_{xx}} = \dfrac{0.29015}{0.1226} = 2.3666$ *[1 mark]*

And the intercept a is given by:

$a = \bar{y} - b\bar{x} = \dfrac{\sum y}{n} - b\dfrac{\sum x}{n} = \dfrac{67.49}{8} - 2.3666 \times \dfrac{26.12}{8} = 0.709$ *[1 mark]*

So the regression line has equation: $y = 2.367x + 0.709$ [1 mark]
To plot the line, find two points that the line passes through. A regression line always passes through $(\bar{x}, \bar{y})$, which here is equal to (3.27, 8.44). Then put $x = 3$ (say) to find that the line also passes through (3, 7.81).
Now plot these points (in circles) on your scatter diagram, and draw the regression line through them [1 mark for plotting the line correctly]

c) (i) *$x = 3.15$, $y = 2.367 \times 3.15 + 0.709 =$ 8.17 (to 3 sig. fig.) [2 marks] — this should be reliable, since we are using interpolation in a known region [1 mark].*
(ii) *$x = 3.88$, $y = 2.367 \times 3.88 + 0.709 =$ 9.89 (to 3 sig. fig.) [2 marks] — this could be unreliable, since we are using extrapolation [1 mark].*

d) (i) *$x = 3.32$, residual $= 8.25 - (2.367 \times 3.32 + 0.709) =$ –0.317 (3 sig. fig.)*
[1 mark for calculation, 1 mark for plotting residual correctly]
(ii) *$x = 3.27$, residual $= 8.59 - (2.367 \times 3.27 + 0.709) =$ 0.141 (3 sig. fig.)*
[1 mark for calculation, 1 mark for plotting residual correctly]

Exam Answers

1 **(a)** The amount of revision (***R***)
(1 mark for correct answer.)

(b) The exam mark (***M***)
(1 mark for correct answer.)

The explanatory variable is also known as the **independent variable** and the response variable as the **dependent variable**. The dependent variable depends on the value of the independent variable.

As usual, a nice gentle start...

2 **(a)** The events are mutually exclusive, so they can't both happen. Hence P(A ∩ B) = ***0***.
(1 mark for the correct answer.)

(b) For mutually exclusive events, P(A ∪ B) = P(A) + P(B). So P(A ∪ B) = 0.3 + 0.4 = ***0.7***.
(2 marks for the correct answer, otherwise 1 mark for quoting the correct formula.)

(c) The probability that neither event happens is equal to 1 – P(A ∪ B) = 1 – 0.7 = ***0.3***.
(2 marks for the correct answer, otherwise 1 mark for using the correct method.)

(d) Now P(A | B) is the probability of A, given that B has already happened. But since A and B are mutually exclusive, they can't both happen — so P(A | B) must equal **zero**.
You can use the formula for conditional probability if you like to get the same answer:

$$P(A \mid B) = \frac{P(A \cap B)}{P(B)} = \frac{0}{P(B)} = \boldsymbol{0}.$$

(1 mark for the correct answer, and 1 mark for a reasonable explanation.)

3 **(a)** p = ***0.2***, since the probabilities have to add up to 1.
(1 mark for the correct answer.)

Easy.

(b) ***Discrete uniform distribution.***
(1 mark for the correct answer.)

Easy.

(c) Now F(25) = P(X ≤ 25), but this is just the same as P(X ≤ 20), because the distribution is discrete. And this is equal to P(X = 0) + P(X = 10) + P(X = 20) = **0.6**.
(2 marks for the correct answer, otherwise 1 mark for some understanding of F(x), the cumulative distribution function.)

Getting harder.

Answers

(d) $E(X) = \sum x P(X = x)$

$= \underline{0.2 \times (0 + 10 + 20 + 50 + 100)}$ $(P(X = x) = 0.2$ for any $x)$

$= \boldsymbol{36}$

$\mathrm{Var}(X) = \sum x^2 P(X = x) - \{E(X)\}^2$

$= \underline{0.2 \times (0 + 100 + 400 + 2500 + 10000) - 36^2}$

$= 2600 - 1296$

$= \boldsymbol{1304}$

(2 marks for each correct answer, otherwise 1 mark for each bit of the underlined working.)

A bit harder.

(e) $\underline{E(3X - 4) = 3E(X) - 4} = 3 \times 36 - 4 = \mathbf{104}$

$\underline{\mathrm{Var}(3X - 4) = 3^2\mathrm{Var}(X)} = 9 \times 1304 = \mathbf{11736}$

(2 marks for each correct answer, otherwise 1 mark for quoting each underlined formula correctly.)

Trickier — especially the variance bit.

(f) Remember, X is a random variable that shows what's paid out. The expected value of X is 36p, so a charge of 40p will only ***average a profit of 4p per game***. This is unlikely to be sufficient to cover the owner's costs.

(1 mark for saying that the expected profit per game is 4p, and 1 mark for any sensible comment.)

Ooh — easy again.

(g) ***Probably not.*** It would be usual for small prizes to have high probabilities and big prizes to have low probabilities.

(1 mark for saying that this model is unlikely, and 1 mark for any sensible explanation as to why.)

Sigh of relief — wasn't as bad as I thought.

4 (a) The mean (μ) is given by $\mu = \dfrac{\sum x}{10} = \dfrac{500}{10} = \boldsymbol{50}$.

The variance (σ^2) is 'the mean of the squares minus the square of the mean'. And the standard deviation (σ) is just the square root of the variance. So the standard deviation is given by

$$\sigma = \underline{\sqrt{\frac{\sum x^2}{n} - \left(\frac{\sum x}{n}\right)^2}} = \underline{\sqrt{\frac{25622}{10} - 50^2}}$$

$$= \sqrt{62.2} = \boldsymbol{7.89} \text{ (to 3 s.f.)}$$

(1 mark for a correct mean and 2 marks for a correct standard deviation. If your standard deviation is wrong, but you get any of the underlined stages correct (or you write down another correct formula for the standard deviation), or you forget to take the square root of the variance, get 1 mark.)

(b) (i) The mean will be ***unchanged***, because the ***new value is equal to the original mean***.

(1 mark for 'unchanged' and 1 mark for a correct explanation.)

(ii) The standard deviation will **decrease**. This is because the variance (and the standard deviation is just the square root of the variance) is a measure of the 'average deviation of the values from the mean'. So by adding a new value that's equal to the mean, you're not adding to the *total deviation* from the mean, but as you have an extra reading, you now have to divide by 11 (not 10) when you work out the variance. This has the effect of decreasing the variance (and hence the standard deviation).

(1 mark for 'decrease' and 1 mark for a correct explanation.)

Remember that bit about the variance being the 'average deviation from the mean'. It can help you get your head round questions like this, where you have to understand what's going on.

5 This is one of those where you have to 'standardise' the normal variable (i.e. subtract the mean and divide by the standard deviation) and use tables for the standard normal variable Z.

(a) ***Find P(X < 7.5).***

$$P(X < 7.5) = P\left(\frac{X - 8}{\sqrt{1.2}} < \frac{7.5 - 8}{\sqrt{1.2}}\right) = P(Z < -0.46)$$

$$= \Phi(-0.46) = 1 - \Phi(0.46)$$

$$= 1 - 0.6772$$

$$= \boldsymbol{0.32} \text{ (to 2 s.f.)}$$

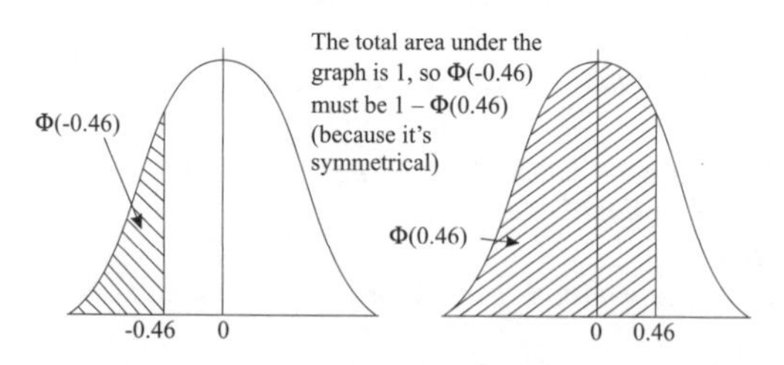

(3 marks for a correct answer, otherwise 1 mark for trying to standardise the normal variable, and 1 mark for correctly reading the table and using the symmetry of the distribution.)

A quick sketch always helps.

Answers

(b) You need to find the probability that the duration is less than 7 minutes or more than 9 minutes.

This is P(X > 9) + P(X < 7).

These are equal by symmetry, so:

$$\underline{P(X<7)+P(X>9)=2P\left(Z<\frac{7-8}{\sqrt{1.2}}\right)}$$

$$=\underline{2P(Z<-0.91)}$$

$$=\underline{2\times\Phi(-0.91)=2\times(1-\Phi(0.91))}$$

$$=2\times(1-0.8186)=\boldsymbol{0.36} \text{ (to 2 s.f.)}$$

(4 marks for the correct answer, otherwise 1 mark for each underlined step correctly shown in working.)

These do definitely get a bit tricky. Just have a good think about what you need to find out before you launch into a load of working out. Getting loads of practice at this kind of question is dead helpful — it gets you used to working with those tables.

(c) You need to find d where: $P(X > d) = 0.01$. It's really the same kind of thing as before.

$$\underline{P(X>d)=0.01, \text{ so } P(X<d)=0.99}$$

$$\underline{\text{i.e. } P\left(Z<\frac{d-8}{\sqrt{1.2}}\right)=0.99.}$$

$$\text{So } \underline{\frac{d-8}{\sqrt{1.2}}=2.3263}, \text{ i.e. } d=\boldsymbol{10.5} \text{ minutes (to 3 s.f.)}$$

(4 marks available for the correct answer, otherwise 1 mark for each underlined step correctly shown in your working.)

These 'standardise the normal variable' questions get everywhere. They look hard, but you soon get used to them. And once you get your head round the basic idea, you'll be able to do pretty much anything they ask you.

6 (a) If C is the event 'has had a crash' and G is the event 'wears glasses', then the tree diagram is as follows:

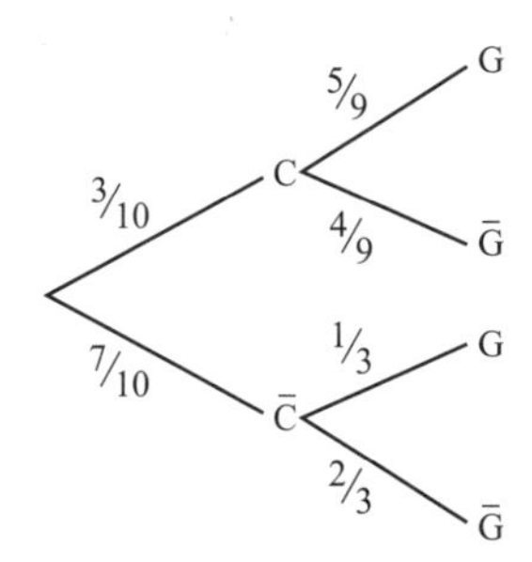

(3 marks available — 1 mark for each correct pair of branches, but lose 1 mark for not cancelling down fractions)

(b) The easiest way is to work out the probabilities of the two branches ending in G by multiplying along each branch, and then adding the results. (In maths-speak, this would be written $P(G) = P(G\cap C) + P(G\cap\bar{C})$, but it's the same thing.)

The probability of 'wearing glasses and having had an accident' (i.e. $P(G\cap C)$) is given by:

$$P(G\cap C)=\frac{3}{10}\times\frac{5}{9}=\frac{15}{90}=\frac{1}{6}.$$

And the probability of 'wearing glasses but not having had an accident' (i.e. $P(G\cap\bar{C})$) is given by:

$$P(G\cap\bar{C})=\frac{7}{10}\times\frac{1}{3}=\frac{7}{30}.$$

Adding these together you get the probability of wearing glasses: $P(G)=\frac{1}{6}+\frac{7}{30}=\frac{5+7}{30}=\frac{12}{30}=\boldsymbol{\frac{2}{5}}$.

(3 marks for a correct answer, otherwise 1 mark for evidence of a correct method, and 1 mark for a correct calculation of either $P(G\cap C)$ or $P(G\cap\bar{C})$.)

(c) You need the formula for conditional probability here:

$P(C\mid G)=\frac{P(C\cap G)}{P(G)}$. Remember that $P(C\cap G)$ is the same as $P(G\cap C)$ (which you've just worked out while you were finding P(G)). Then just plug in the numbers:

$$P(C\mid G)=\frac{1/6}{2/5}=\frac{1}{6}\times\frac{5}{2}=\boldsymbol{\frac{5}{12}}.$$

(3 marks for a correct answer, otherwise 1 mark for substituting in each correct probability.)

Tree diagrams are things you've definitely seen before, and they don't get any harder. The question may sound more complicated, but it's not really.

7 (a) Let H be hard centre, N be nutty and S be soft centre.

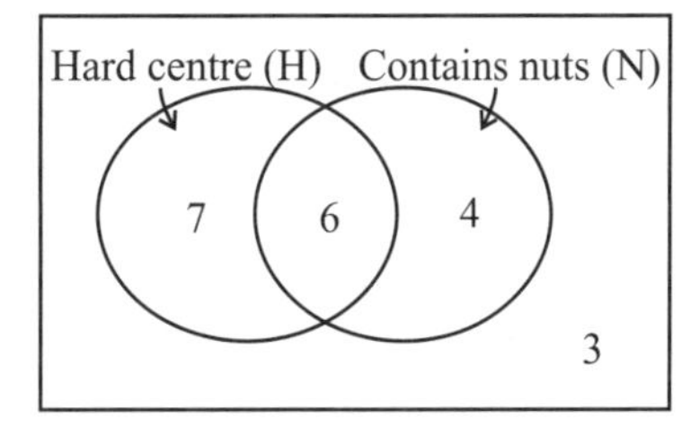

Other answers are possible, e.g. showing S and N instead of H and N.

(2 marks for a correct diagram, otherwise 1 mark for 2 numbers correctly entered.)

Answers

(b) (i) $P(S) = \dfrac{\text{Number of soft centres}}{\text{Total number of chocolates}} = \dfrac{4+3}{20} = \mathbf{\dfrac{7}{20}}$

(1 mark for correct answer.)

(ii) This is a conditional probability question.

$$P(H|N) = \underline{\frac{P(H \cap N)}{P(N)}} = \underline{\frac{N(H \cap N)/20}{N(N)/20}} = \frac{6}{10} = \mathbf{\frac{3}{5}},$$

where N(H) is the number of outcomes in set H, etc.

(3 marks for the correct answer, otherwise 1 mark for each underlined stage correct or equivalent.)

You can do these by counting the number of outcomes in each part of your Venn diagram. That's probably the easiest way. So, for example, in (b) (ii) just use:

$$P(H|N) = \frac{\text{number with nuts and hard centre}}{\text{total number with nuts}}$$

(c) You need the probability of exactly 1 hard centre, but there are three different ways for this to occur — the hard centre could be first out of the box, or second or third. Out of the 20 chocolates, 13 have hard centres, so

$$P(\text{exactly 1 hard centre}) = 3 \times \frac{13}{20} \times \frac{7}{19} \times \frac{6}{18}$$

$$= 3 \times \underline{\frac{13 \times 7 \times 6}{20 \times 19 \times 18}} = \frac{1638}{6840}$$

$$= \mathbf{\frac{91}{380}}$$

$$= \mathbf{0.239} \text{ (to 3 s.f.)}$$

You could work out P(HSS) + P(SHS) + P(SSH), but it's quicker and easier to do it as above. (If you try doing it this way, you'll find you end up adding together three lots of the underlined fraction above, only the numbers in the top line will be in different orders.)

(3 marks for a correct answer, otherwise 1 mark for multiplying 3 suitable fractions together, and 1 mark for multiplying the outcome by 3. Alternatively, 1 mark for trying to find the 3 suitable fractions to add together, and 2 marks for finding the 3 fractions.)

Don't forget that the hard centre could be the first one picked out of the box, or the second or the third — and you need to take the fact that there are 'different arrangements' into account when you work out your probability.

8 (a) The total probability must be 1, so go through all the possible values of x and add the probabilities:

$$\frac{k}{6} + \frac{2k}{6} + \frac{3k}{6} + \frac{3k}{6} + \frac{2k}{6} + \frac{k}{6} = \frac{12k}{6} = 2k.$$

This must equal 1, so k must be $\mathbf{\frac{1}{2}}$.

(3 marks for the correct answer, otherwise 1 mark for stating that the probabilities must add up to 1, and 1 mark for adding the probabilities correctly.)

(b) It's worth making a quick table at this point, just to show the numerical probabilities:

x	1	2	3	4	5	6
P(X=x)	$\frac{1}{12}$	$\frac{2}{12}$	$\frac{3}{12}$	$\frac{3}{12}$	$\frac{2}{12}$	$\frac{1}{12}$

Now $F(3) = P(X \le 3)$, i.e. F(3) is the probability that X takes a value less than or equal to 3.

This is: $F(3) = P(X=1) + P(X=2) + P(X=3)$.

$$= \frac{1}{12} + \frac{2}{12} + \frac{3}{12} = \frac{6}{12} = \mathbf{\frac{1}{2}}$$

(2 marks for the correct answer, otherwise 1 mark for evidence of a suitable method.)

(c) The expected value of a random variable is given by: $E(X) = \sum xP(X = x) = \sum xp(x)$. So here the expected value is:

$$E(X) = \left(1 \times \tfrac{1}{12}\right) + \left(2 \times \tfrac{2}{12}\right) + \left(3 \times \tfrac{3}{12}\right) + \left(4 \times \tfrac{3}{12}\right) + \left(5 \times \tfrac{2}{12}\right) + \left(6 \times \tfrac{1}{12}\right)$$

$$= \frac{1}{12} + \frac{4}{12} + \frac{9}{12} + \frac{12}{12} + \frac{10}{12} + \frac{6}{12}$$

$$= \frac{42}{12} = \frac{7}{2} = 3.5$$

(2 marks available — get 1 mark for each of two valid steps in your method.)

(d) (i) $E(2 - 3X) = 2 - 3E(X) = 2 - (3 \times 3.5) = \mathbf{-8.50}$ (2 d.p.)

$\text{Var}(2 - 3X) = 3^2 \times \text{Var}(X) = 9 \times \left(\frac{23}{12}\right) = \mathbf{17.25}$ (2 d.p.)

(4 marks available — 2 marks for a correct answer, otherwise 1 mark for a suitable method, for each calculation.)

The expected value formula is kind of what you'd expect. But be careful with the variance formula — it's a bit weird.

(ii) $\text{Var}(X) = E(X^2) - \{E(X)\}^2$ (i.e. the variance is the 'mean of the squares minus the square of the mean'). This is a dead useful result to remember, by the way.

Rearranging you get $E(X^2) = \text{Var}(X) + \{E(X)\}^2$, so:

$$E(X^2) = \text{Var}(X) + \left(\tfrac{7}{2}\right)^2 = \frac{23}{12} + \frac{49}{4}$$

$$= \mathbf{\frac{85}{6}} (= 14.17 \text{ (2 d.p.)})$$

(3 marks for the right answer, otherwise 1 mark for rearranging the variance formula above and 1 mark for correctly substituting in the numbers.)

That formula for the variance is a really handy one to remember — or have I said that already...

S1 MATHEMATICS FORMULA SHEET

The formula booklet you'll get in your exam won't be the same as this.
It'll have a few more statistical formulas, plus a load of other stuff you won't need for S1.

Probability

$$P(A \cup B) = P(A) + P(B) - P(A \cap B)$$
$$P(A \cap B) = P(A)P(B \mid A)$$

Discrete distributions

For a discrete random variable X taking values x_i with probabilities p_i

Expectation (mean): $\mathrm{E}(X) = \mu = \sum x_i p_i$

Variance: $\mathrm{Var}(X) = \sigma^2 = \sum (x_i - \mu)^2 p_i = \sum x_i^2 p_i - \mu^2$

The normal distribution function

The cumulative distribution function $\Phi(z)$ is tabulated below. This is defined as $\Phi(z) = \frac{1}{\sqrt{2\pi}} \int_{-\infty}^{z} e^{-\frac{1}{2}t^2} \, dt$.

z	$\Phi(z)$	Z	$\Phi(z)$	z	$\Phi(z)$	z	$\Phi(z)$	z	$\Phi(z)$	z	$\Phi(z)$	z	$\Phi(z)$
0.00	0.5000	0.34	0.6331	0.68	0.7517	1.00	0.8413	1.34	0.9099	1.68	0.9535	2.00	0.9772
0.01	0.5040	0.35	0.6368	0.69	0.7549	1.01	0.8438	1.35	0.9115	1.69	0.9545	2.02	0.9783
0.02	0.5080	0.36	0.6406	0.70	0.7580	1.02	0.8461	1.36	0.9131	1.70	0.9554	2.04	0.9793
0.03	0.5120	0.37	0.6443	0.71	0.7611	1.03	0.8485	1.37	0.9147	1.71	0.9564	2.06	0.9803
0.04	0.5160	0.38	0.6480	0.72	0.7642	1.04	0.8508	1.38	0.9162	1.72	0.9573	2.08	0.9812
0.05	0.5199	0.39	0.6517	0.73	0.7673	1.05	0.8531	1.39	0.9177	1.73	0.9582	2.10	0.9821
0.06	0.5239	0.40	0.6554	0.74	0.7704	1.06	0.8554	1.40	0.9192	1.74	0.9591	2.12	0.9830
0.07	0.5279	0.41	0.6591	0.75	0.7734	1.07	0.8577	1.41	0.9207	1.75	0.9599	2.14	0.9838
0.08	0.5319	0.42	0.6628	0.76	0.7764	1.08	0.8599	1.42	0.9222	1.76	0.9608	2.16	0.9846
0.09	0.5359	0.43	0.6664	0.77	0.7794	1.09	0.8621	1.43	0.9236	1.77	0.9616	2.18	0.9854
0.10	0.5398	0.44	0.6700	0.78	0.7823	1.10	0.8643	1.44	0.9251	1.78	0.9625	2.20	0.9861
0.11	0.5438	0.45	0.6736	0.79	0.7852	1.11	0.8665	1.45	0.9265	1.79	0.9633	2.22	0.9868
0.12	0.5478	0.46	0.6772	0.80	0.7881	1.12	0.8686	1.46	0.9279	1.80	0.9641	2.24	0.9875
0.13	0.5517	0.47	0.6808	0.81	0.7910	1.13	0.8708	1.47	0.9292	1.81	0.9649	2.26	0.9881
0.14	0.5557	0.48	0.6844	0.82	0.7939	1.14	0.8729	1.48	0.9306	1.82	0.9656	2.28	0.9887
0.15	0.5596	0.49	0.6879	0.83	0.7967	1.15	0.8749	1.49	0.9319	1.83	0.9664	2.30	0.9893
0.16	0.5636	0.50	0.6915	0.84	0.7995	1.16	0.8770	1.50	0.9332	1.84	0.9671	2.35	0.9906
0.17	0.5675	0.51	0.6950	0.85	0.8023	1.17	0.8790	1.51	0.9345	1.85	0.9678	2.40	0.9918
0.18	0.5714	0.52	0.6985	0.86	0.8051	1.18	0.8810	1.52	0.9357	1.86	0.9686	2.50	0.9938
0.19	0.5753	0.53	0.7019	0.87	0.8078	1.19	0.8830	1.53	0.9370	1.87	0.9693	2.60	0.9953
0.20	0.5793	0.54	0.7054	0.88	0.8106	1.20	0.8849	1.54	0.9382	1.88	0.9699	2.70	0.9965
0.21	0.5832	0.55	0.7088	0.89	0.8133	1.21	0.8869	1.55	0.9394	1.89	0.9706	2.80	0.9974
0.22	0.5871	0.56	0.7123	0.90	0.8159	1.22	0.8888	1.56	0.9406	1.90	0.9713	2.90	0.9981
0.23	0.5910	0.57	0.7157	0.91	0.8186	1.23	0.8907	1.57	0.9418	1.91	0.9719	3.00	0.9987
0.24	0.5948	0.58	0.7190	0.92	0.8212	1.24	0.8925	1.58	0.9429	1.92	0.9726	3.10	0.9990
0.25	0.5987	0.59	0.7224	0.93	0.8238	1.25	0.8944	1.59	0.9441	1.93	0.9732	3.20	0.9993
0.26	0.6026	0.60	0.7257	0.94	0.8264	1.26	0.8962	1.60	0.9452	1.94	0.9738	3.30	0.9995
0.27	0.6064	0.61	0.7291	0.95	0.8289	1.27	0.8980	1.61	0.9463	1.95	0.9744	3.40	0.9997
0.28	0.6103	0.62	0.7324	0.96	0.8315	1.28	0.8997	1.62	0.9474	1.96	0.9750	3.50	0.9998
0.29	0.6141	0.63	0.7357	0.97	0.8340	1.29	0.9015	1.63	0.9484	1.97	0.9756	3.60	0.9998
0.30	0.6179	0.64	0.7389	0.98	0.8365	1.30	0.9032	1.64	0.9495	1.98	0.9761	3.70	0.9999
0.31	0.6217	0.65	0.7422	0.99	0.8389	1.31	0.9049	1.65	0.9505	1.99	0.9767	3.80	0.9999
0.32	0.6255	0.66	0.7454	1.00	0.8413	1.32	0.9066	1.66	0.9515	2.00	0.9772	3.90	1.0000
0.33	0.6293	0.67	0.7486			1.33	0.9082	1.67	0.9525			4.00	1.0000

Percentage points of the normal distribution

The z-values in the table are those which a random variable $Z \sim \mathrm{N}(0, 1)$ exceeds with probability p, i.e. $\mathrm{P}(Z > z) = 1 - \Phi(z) = p$.

p	z	p	z
0.5000	0.0000	0.0500	1.6449
0.4000	0.2533	0.0250	1.9600
0.3000	0.5244	0.0100	2.3263
0.2000	0.8416	0.0050	2.5758
0.1500	1.0364	0.0010	3.0902
0.1000	1.2816	0.0005	3.2905

Index

A HANDBOOK FOR SPECIAL NEEDS ASSISTANTS

Working in Partnership with Teachers

GLENYS FOX

David Fulton Publishers
in association with
Hampshire COUNTY COUNCIL

David Fulton Publishers Ltd
414 Chiswick High Road, London W4 5TF

www.fultonpublishers.co.uk

First published in Great Britain by
David Fulton Publishers 1993
Reprinted 1993, 1994 (three times), 1995, 1996 (twice), 1997, 1998 (twice), 1999, 2000 (twice), 2001, 2002, 2003

Note: The right of the author to be identified as the author of this work has been asserted by her in accordance with the Copyright, Designs and Patents Act 1988.

Copyright © Hampshire County Council Education Department

British Library Cataloguing in Publication Data

A catalogue record for this book is available from the British Library

ISBN 1–85346–286–1

All rights reserved. No part of this publication may be reproduced, stored in a retrieval system or transmitted, in any form, or by any means, electronic, mechanical, photocopying, recording or otherwise, without the prior permission of the publishers.

Designed by Almac Ltd, London

Typeset by RP Typesetters Ltd, Unit 13, 21 Wren Street, London WC1X 0HF

Printed in Great Britain by Ashford Colour Press Ltd, Gosport, Hants

Contents

Acknowledgements

I am indebted to a number of valued colleagues in the Hampshire County Council Education Department for inspiration, which has led to the production of this handbook. I would like to record particular thanks to Ahmad Ramjhun, Educational Psychologist, for his work with me over the past four years in supporting the training of special needs assistants. Also to John Bailey, Olivia Colvin, Jean Samuel and Sue Stares of the Special Educational Needs Advisory and Support Service for their enthusiasm and commitment to meeting the special needs of special needs assistants.

In this handbook I have quoted from *Getting the Act Together: Provision for Pupils with Special Educational Needs* and the extracts I have used are reproduced with kind permission of the Controller of Her Majesty's Stationery Office. My thanks also to James Quinnell for the cartoons which illustrate some of the text, and to Eleanor Olson for typing the manuscript.

I have had the good fortune to work closely with three wonderful special needs assistants, Christine Cann, Jan Hall and Ann Keeping, during my years spent teaching and I owe them grateful thanks for sharing the ups and downs of classroom life and for keeping me sane!

Glenys Fox
Senior Educational Psychologist
Hampshire County Council Education Department
June 1993

Purpose

The purpose of this handbook is to enable special needs assistants to work more effectively in supporting:

* the pupil with special needs

* the class teacher

* the school

Audience

This handbook is intended as a resource for:

* non-teaching staff who support pupils with special needs (usually known as special needs assistants, learning support assistants, teacher assistants, special schools assistants or welfare assistants)

* teachers who work with special needs assistants

Overview

There are sections on:

* roles and responsibilities

* giving support

* different kinds of special need

* working with colleagues to support learning

Introduction

In 1988 a survey of Southampton schools highlighted a pressing need for the training and support of special needs assistants (SNAs). These school helpers were perceived by schools as having enormous enthusiasm and dedication to children but as being undervalued in respect of support, training and development needs.

A training course was, therefore, devised by the Educational Psychology Service, together with the Special Educational Needs Advisory and Support Service. This course was piloted in 1991 and is now linked to a City and Guilds qualification - the 'Certificate in Learning Support' (732-1).*

Those of us involved in the training and support of special needs assistants have been overwhelmed by the enthusiasm of these people. We have become aware of the potential of this valuable human resource which remains all to often 'untapped' and inefficiently used in our schools. The importance of giving support and guidance to assistants is clear. They are frequently working very closely with some very needy children whose quality of school experience can depend quite significantly on the knowledge and skills of the assistant.

The responsibility for support of these assistants lies primarily with the school staff and there is undoubtedly scope for schools to make more effective use of these valuable people. Indeed, the recent management handbook from the Audit Commission/HMI entitled *Getting the Act Together* recognises supporting adults as 'an expensive resource, the use of which should be prepared in advance if the cost is to be justified'. Teachers who work with SNAs have a direct influence on the deployment of this resource and should acknowledge this responsibility.

Local Education Authorities (LEAs) have a role in encouraging appropriate training, in recognising expertise and in providing security of tenure for special needs assistants. This role is being increasingly recognised as numbers of such assistants continue to grow.

This handbook has sprung out of the work done with special needs assistants over the past four years. It is intended as a practical guide containing useful information which SNAs and teachers working with SNAs need to know. It is complementary to training rather than a substitute for it.

So, if you are a special needs assistant or intend to become one, this handbook should help you in providing information about your role and about some of the special needs you may come across.

* Further details about the course can be obtained from the author at the following address:-

Hampshire Educational Psychology Service, S. W. Division, Education Department, Hampshire County Council, Arundel Towers North, Portland Terrace, Southampton SO9 4XE.

CHAPTER 1

Special educational needs

What is meant by Special Educational Need?

The 1981 Education Act states that:

> 'A child has special educational needs if he or she has a learning difficulty which may be a result of a physical or sensory disability, an emotional or behavioural problem or developmental delay' (1981 Education Act, Section I).

This significant Act helped to change ideas about children with difficulties. Before the 1981 Act, children had been categorised and labelled according to their 'handicap'.

The 1981 Act:

- changed the focus away from labelling the child;
- placed the focus on the extent to which a learning difficulty stops a child from learning with other children of the same age;
- placed the focus on the child's special educational needs in terms of the special educational provision required to help them learn;
- stressed that 'special educational needs' is a relative term which arises from the interaction between a child and his or her environment.

The idea of a child's needs being related to the school's ability to meet the needs was a new perspective which helped teachers to see that a child's difficulties do not always start from within the child. Sometimes, difficulties are caused because the school cannot provide the learning tasks or levels of support which are necessary to meet the needs, and sometimes needs are in fact created because the school is not able to be flexible. Thus the *interaction* between the child and his or her environment is now considered crucial in any discussion about special educational needs.

Children who have special educational needs are now described often in terms of learning difficulties, emotional and behavioural difficulties, physical disabilities, sensory impairment, language difficulties or communication impairment. Sometimes children may have special needs arising from a combination of these factors.

Why do we need Special Needs Assistants?

The 1981 Act states that:

> 'Where possible, all children with special educational needs should be

educated in ordinary schools', and

'For integration to be effective, pupils with special needs must be engaged in all or most of the activities of the school. Some pupils with special educational needs require extra help if they are to benefit from the experiences available to all pupils'.

Special needs assistants (SNAs) often provide this 'extra help' which makes it possible for children to go to ordinary schools. Since the 1981 Act, many children who might previously have been educated in special schools have been maintained in ordinary (i.e. mainstream) schools. The majority of these pupils require some additional support in order to make the best use of the opportunities offered to them in mainstream schools. We need SNAs to support these children in schools, children who, without this support, would not cope with the demands of ordinary school life.

Since 1981, the number of such assistants has grown considerably, e.g. Hampshire has nearly 2000 special needs assistants and special school assistants working in local authority schools. Special schools have always employed classroom assistants to support those pupils whose needs are most severe and who benefit from small class sizes and high levels of adult support.

What is a 'Statement'?

Many SNAs now work for some of their time with pupils who have a 'Statement of Special Educational Need'. This is a document issued by the local education authority which details what the special needs of the child are considered to be and what should be provided in order to meet those needs.

The Warnock Report (1978) - a report about special needs which influenced the philosophy of the 1981 Act - estimated that about 20 per cent (1 in 5) of all pupils will have some kind of special educational need at some time during their school life, ranging from very mild to very severe. It was also estimated that only 2 per cent (1 in 50) pupils would have such severe and complex difficulties that additional resources or special schooling would be necessary in order to meet their needs. If significant additional resources or special schooling are required, a statement is issued about the needs of the child. There are an estimated 1.2 million pupils in local authority schools in England and Wales who have special educational needs and, of these, nearly 170,000 have a formal statement of need.

Most children with special educational needs can have their needs met fully from the resources already available in all mainstream schools. There is a gradual and detailed process of assessment and response which involves the following stages:

- assessment by the class teacher;
- consultation and support from the school's special needs co-ordinator and other staff (the SNA is often involved in this consultation and support);
- advice from educational psychologists and/or special needs support teachers;

- direct involvement with the child by educational psychologists and possibly specialist support teachers.

At each of these stages there is a need to record and review what is being done, and to inform the parents.

Following these stages of assessment, if it is considered that additional resources are necessary to meet the child's needs, then *Formal Assessment* is initiated. Reports about the child are collated from:

- the parents - PARENTAL ADVICE
- the school - EDUCATIONAL ADVICE
- the school medical officer - MEDICAL ADVICE
- the educational psychologist - PSYCHOLOGICAL ADVICE.

Reports may also be sought from:

- social services
- specialist teachers
- education welfare services
- speech therapist
- physiotherapist
- child psychiatrist,

if the child is known to these services.

This advice is carefully considered and, should the advice indicate, a Statement of Special Educational Need is issued.

CHAPTER 2

The role of the special needs assistant

What are my responsibilities?

It is important to realise that the class teacher has the responsibility for the education of *all* children in his or her class, and the head teacher has responsibility for all the children in the school.

The child with special needs with whom you may be employed to work is likely to need specialised learning or behaviour programmes. The class teacher has the responsibility to ensure that appropriate programmes are being planned, followed and monitored. You are expected to work under the guidance of the class teacher to meet the needs of the child.

There may be occasions when you are expected to work on your own with one or more children. In this situation you need to behave as a responsible adult in ensuring the well-being of each child.

What if something goes wrong?

Every employee of the local authority is covered by a general employment insurance policy held by that authority. By law, you are deemed a 'responsible adult' and the duties performed by you are delegated to you by the head teacher. If something does go wrong, you should discuss the situation with the teacher who is responsible for your work and with the head teacher. In the case of any accident, it must be recorded in the school's incident/accident book. In the case of injury to a child, your first priority is to see that the child is given first aid and that the class teacher is informed.

If, during the course of your work with a child, some disclosure of physical or sexual abuse is made, then you have a duty, under the Child Protection laws, to inform the head teacher who will take any action necessary. The 1989 Children Act states that the child's welfare is paramount and safeguarding and promoting it is a priority.

Schools have clear routines to be followed in the case of injury or abuse and it is your responsibility to ensure that you know what these procedures are. If you are not sure, the class teacher you normally work with can direct you to the information.

You may consider that membership of a union will be useful in providing you with back-up support, should things go badly wrong.

What is my role in the school?

The role of the special needs assistant will vary from school to school, depending on the organisation and on the individual child, or groups of children, concerned. It is important that you know what your duties are from the start in relation to different pupils.

You need to know whether you are working mainly with one child or are expected to work with small groups, or sometimes with the whole class. An up-to-date job description is certainly necessary in providing you with a description of your duties (a possible job description is provided in Appendix A).

It is frequently the case that SNAs are 'thrown in at the deep end', with no clear idea of what is expected of them. This leads to feelings of confusion and of being undervalued.

This can be prevented by:

- a clear job description (see Appendix A);
- communication between the class teacher and the SNA, so that the SNA is clear about:

i) the ground rules for working with the teacher;
ii) the individual plan for the pupil.

What are the ground rules?

These are the guidelines for you to use in working with a particular teacher. Teachers will have their own ideas and you need to ask about these before you start, so that you can reduce confusion and provide a consistent approach. Also, you need to know what authority you have when working in the classroom. The more you understand the workings of the class and the way the teacher operates, the easier it will be for you to work within the class and to support the children with special needs.

Here are some suggestions of questions to ask in order to determine 'ground rules':

(1) *How shall I be introduced to the class?*
It is important that you are, in fact, introduced to the class rather than just being seen to 'pop up' from time to time. It is also important that you are introduced in the right way so that pupils' perception of your role is clear. Discuss this with the class teacher.
An introduction such as: 'This is Mrs. Smith and she is Andrew's special helper' is probably not helpful, both in terms of Andrew being pointed out as 'special' and of raising the idea of Mrs. Smith as some kind of 'minder'. A more useful introduction might be: 'This is Mrs.Smith who will be working with me to help you all to do your best. Sometimes, she will work with one or two of you and sometimes with small groups'.

(2) *How do I work with other pupils?*
Even though you may be only responsible for one pupil, the others will note your presence and will be curious. You should be prepared to tell them something about yourself and, as far as

possible, treat all pupils in the class in, generally, the same way, giving help to them as well as to your pupil, if they ask for it. You should encourage them to accept your pupil as a full member of the class.

(3) *Can I give pupils permission?*
e.g. when a child asks to go to the toilet, can I give that permission?
It is likely that children will ask your permission on frequent occasions about how to act in certain situations. Discuss any such scenarios with the class teacher so that you know what to do.

(4) *Can I 'mark' books?*
e.g. when a child comes to show me some written work, when is it appropriate for me to put a mark on their work?
It is likely that this will be acceptable for you to do when working individually or in small groups with children but, generally, the class teacher will need to do this.

(5) *Where shall I sit in the classroom?*
e.g. when is it appropriate for me to sit right by the pupil and when should I stay at a distance?
This will depend on the particular activity and you will learn, with practice, when it is necessary to give individual support and when to withdraw and allow the pupil some independence.

(6) *What shall I do if I see some misbehaviour?*
e.g. when two children are getting at each other, shall I intervene and, if so, what sort of approach should I use?
There are bound to be occasions when you see things going on of which the teacher is unaware. You need to negotiate with the class teacher how you should react to such situations, and know when it is appropriate to refer the situation to the class teacher rather than deal with it yourself.

(7) *What is the best use of my time?*
e.g. should I sit in on school assemblies when I am not really needed?
You need to negotiate a timetable which is able to use your support to best effect and to agree with the teacher when your presence is needed and when it might be of more use for you to be preparing materials for the pupil or pupils you support, e.g. in assembly time or when pupils are watching video materials.

What is the individual programme for the pupil?

Every pupil with a special need, whether statemented or not, should have some special arrangements made for them. You need to know, before you start working with the pupil, the particular needs of the pupil and how you can help in meeting those needs. Remember that it is the responsibility of the head teacher to provide a programme and this is usually delegated to the class teacher.

If the pupil has a statement of special educational need, then it will be helpful if you can read this document as it will provide useful background information and will detail the main areas of difficulty for the pupil. All pupils with statements are reviewed annually, to determine whether or not their needs remain the same and to make plans for meeting the needs in the future. This should provide up-to-date information. If you do not understand some of the terms used, then ask for these to be explained.

Pupils who are not statemented, but who also have special needs, should have some written school records of what their needs are and what action is considered necessary to meet the needs. Schools are becoming much more aware of the value of recording information about pupils with special needs and of planning ahead. The management handbook from the Audit Commission/HMI entitled *Getting the Act Together* recommends:

> *Schools and teachers should plan the use of extra adult support for pupils with special needs.*
> Where extra adult help is provided, planning and communication are the keys to improving its impact. If a small amount of the time spent alongside pupils were redirected into planning and discussion about individual pupils between support and classroom teachers, there would be a significant improvement in effectiveness.

Effective work with such pupils involves regular meetings of class teacher, special needs assistant and, if appropriate, the special needs co-ordinator in the school and/or the parent. At these meetings, it is essential to set goals or objectives so that you know what you are aiming for. You might find it useful to ask the following questions about the pupil:

- Have the needs changed since the last review?
- What are the current areas of concern?
- What are the areas to concentrate on in the next few weeks? e.g.
  • learning to spell simple three-letter words;
  • learning to work for five minutes without getting up out of seat.
- What materials, games or resources will be necessary to achieve the goals?
- Where is it best to work with the pupil?
  • inside the classroom alongside the pupil?
  • with a small group inside the class?
  • outside the class alone or in a small group?
- When should these sessions take place during the school day?
- Who should be involved?
  • which pupils in which groups?
  • whether class teacher or SNA should work with the 'special group'.
- How will the pupils' progress be recorded and monitored?
- When will the next review take place?

Together with the class teacher, you need to evaluate (review) how effective the arrangements have been in the past in order to make improvements for future programmes. Through this process, you will find out what does and doesn't work for the child and learn how best to meet his or her needs. This process will also enable you to assess how well you are doing your job in supporting the child.

This section can be summarised as follows:

Working together {Class Teacher, SNA} + Effective Learning Programme = SUCCESS

CHAPTER 3

Giving support

Eighty special needs assistants were asked to define their supporting role (SNA in-service training courses 1991 and 1992: Certificate in Learning Support, Hampshire) Their responses fell into three main categories:

- supporting the pupil
- supporting the teacher
- supporting the school.

How can I support the pupil?

SNAs identified the following aspects of their supportive role with pupils:

- promoting independence
- inspiring confidence and trust
- valuing the child
- fostering peer group acceptance
- encouraging and giving rewards
- developing listening skills
- enabling the child
- knowing the background
- finding out about the special need
- keeping confidences
- being 'in tune' with the child's physical needs.

Promoting independence

This is a key concept in considering your role. You are there to give a high level of support initially, but as time goes on, you must be seeking to encourage the pupil to attempt new tasks without your support. It is common for SNAs to feel that they must always be 'one step ahead' but, in fact, the idea of being 'one step behind' is much more helpful in promoting the independence of the pupil. If you are always foreseeing pitfalls and removing them from the path of the pupil, then he or she will never learn strategies for coping in the real world.

However, there will be times when you will have to act in order to pre-empt serious situations - common sense is a necessary quality!

Some special needs assistants feel that if they are employed to support one particular pupil, then it is appropriate to stick like glue to that pupil. Though there are times when the child will need individual support, it will often be appropriate to help the pupil within a small group or even to spend time standing back and observing the behaviour of the pupil in classroom situations. You may be surprised at how much he or she is capable of. You will be doing the child no favours if you encourage dependence on you. In fact, you should be aiming to be so effective in promoting the independence of the pupil that you work yourself out of a job!

Inspiring confidence and trust

Often, it is the case that pupils with special educational needs are lacking in confidence. Children become aware of failure very quickly and they lose confidence when they see their classmates making progress while they struggle. Pupils who have had difficult social histories may feel that they have been 'let down' by the important adults in their lives and feel it is hard to trust someone to be consistent, fair and encouraging. A pupil with a low opinion of himself or herself, for whatever reason, is going to begin to expect to fail. It is, therefore, vital that you take every opportunity to point out what the pupil is good at and to lead them to expect that they can succeed. Think out ways of providing frequent opportunities for real success. It may take time but if you have a consistent, positive and fair attitude towards the child, he or she will learn to develop confidence and to trust you.

Valuing the child

No child can learn effectively when they are not feeling valued. It is a key role of a special needs assistant to value the child. Any child who is thought of as 'different' from other pupils may encounter negative attitudes particularly if the disability is obvious. Surviving childhood teasing is often dependent on self-esteem, so it is very important that the child needs to feel secure and highly regarded by the important people in his or her life - and you are one of them.

Fostering peer group acceptance

It is part of your role to encourage the other pupils to value the child. This entails drawing attention to those skills the child is good at, or to some particular achievement of the child. It may also involve valuing the contributions of the child, e.g. making the child group leader in appropriate activities. Some children need help to improve social skills, i.e. the way they relate to others. If the child you work with has poor social skills then you can help him or her by practising appropriate responses - first in play-acting then in real situations. For younger children it might be helpful to act out a well-known fairy tale, e.g. Billy Goats Gruff, with each child being able to take on different roles. This can help children explore feelings and relationships - the troll seen as a 'bully' and the little billy goat Gruff seen as the 'victim'. This sort of activity can lead on to discussions about feelings and about rights and wrongs. For older pupils, discussing real situations and then role playing to consider the best outcomes can be extremely helpful.

Encouraging and giving rewards

Giving the pupil encouragement and praise is a very important part of your role and will contribute in a large part to the development of self-esteem and confidence. Liberal amounts of praise ***must*** be given. Meaningful praise means telling the pupil *why* you are pleased with him or her, e.g. it is better to say 'Gemma, I like the way you have used colour in this picture' rather than 'That's a good picture', or 'Tom, you listened to the story well today' rather than just 'Good boy'.

All children respond to rewards if the rewards are motivating and achievable. It will help you in your work with the pupil if you can work out, early on in your relationship, what it is that motivates him or her. It may be that just a word of praise will be enough but, frequently, with pupils who have experienced failure, it needs to be accompanied by something tangible. Here are some ideas you might suggest to the child as incentives, but remember to ask the child first what they would like as a reward once they have achieved what you have negotiated.

Ideas for rewards

Primary age pupils

- extra 'choosing time', when he or she can choose an activity;
- extra time on the computer;
- a favourite game;
- a bubble-blowing session;
- making biscuits, cakes or sweets;
- stickers to wear and keep;
- decorating plain biscuits with icing and 'sprinkles';
- doing an 'important' job for the class teacher or head teacher;
- music while you work;
- letter or certificate sent home to parents.

Secondary age pupils

- extra time on the computer;
- letter or certificate sent home to parents;
- position of responsibility;
- a special interest project;
- free ticket to school disco.

It is important to ensure that the reward is achievable over a short period of time to start with, so that success is encouraged. For younger children particularly, the reward needs to be earned within one day so that it is immediate. Other children may be able to work towards a reward at the end of two or three days, or at the end of a week. Again, you will need to negotiate this with the class teacher so that there is consistency in your approach.

Developing listening skills

When you start work with a pupil, it is tempting to do a lot of the talking and to expect that the pupil has taken in what you have said. Remember that effective communication is a two-way process and that some children need time to get their thoughts together and to express themselves. Some are only able to understand short bits of information at a time. You may need to check out that the pupil has understood by asking him or her to repeat back to you the information you have given.

Pupils with emotional difficulties can be helped enormously by someone providing a 'listening ear'. This means that when the pupil is talking, you give him or her your full attention and are able to make encouraging gestures such as nodding and smiling. Non-verbal 'messages' from you to the child are, in fact, more important than the words you use.

You can learn to encourage pupils to talk by choosing the right phrases. This is called Active Listening. Brenda Mallon, in her book *An Introduction to Counselling Skills for Special Educational Needs* gives the following examples:

Listening Skills

Types	*Purpose*	*Examples*
Warmth, Support	To help the pupil	'I'd like to help you, are you able to tell me about what is the matter?'
Clarification	To get the complete 'story' from the pupil	'Can you tell me more about it?' 'Do you mean..............?'
Restatement	To check our meaning is the same as the pupil's	'From what you are saying, I understand that ....'
Encouragement	To encourage the pupil	'I realise this is difficult for you but you are doing really well'
Reflective	To act as a mirror so the pupil can see what is being communicated.	'You feel that.....................' 'It was very hard for you to accept....................'
	To help pupils evaluate their feelings.	'You felt angry and upset when ....'
	To show you understand the feelings behind the words.	'I can see you are feeling upset........'
Summarising	To bring together the points raised.	'These are the main things you have told me.....' 'As I see it, your main worry seems to be ....'

If you are able to use some of these skills then you will be well on the way to being a good listener and more than that, you will help the pupil to work through whatever is causing worry or concern.

Enabling the child

The pupil with special needs often feels unable to attempt tasks which other pupils have no problem with. Your role is *not* to do the task for the pupil, but to enable the pupil to do that task for himself or herself by providing the necessary 'tools for the job'. This may mean:

- explaining the task clearly when the pupil has not understood (if the problem persists, see the teacher);
- making sure the pupil knows what equipment is necessary, where it is kept and how to use it;
- helping the pupil to organise his/her thoughts and consider how to set out the work;
- encouraging the pupil to arrive at the lesson on time and with the correct equipment;
- giving the pupil strategies to use to help him/her remember information, e.g. writing lists, keeping a diary;
- working with small groups to encourage sharing and co-operation.

Your role is *not* to do the task for the pupil!

"Yes — well done Mrs Smith, you got 10/10 for those sums!"

Knowing the background

You will understand the pupil's difficulties better if you know something about the pupil's home life and the way he or she spends time out of school.

It will help you in establishing a relationship if you find out early on who the other family members are, whether the pupil has any pets and what hobbies or special interests he or she has. You may find it valuable, particularly with younger children, to keep a scrapbook entitled 'All About Me', into which you can put photographs and snippets of written information about what happens in the life of the child. The child will feel valued when you show interest in the things which are meaningful to him or her. For the older child this can also be a useful activity. Writing an autobiography 'My Life Story' can be particularly helpful to pupils who have emotional difficulties and low self-esteem.

"Show an interest in the child's interests . . ."

Finding out about the special need

It is the responsibility of the class teacher or the special needs co-ordinator in the school to ensure that you know what you need to know about the particular special need, in order to do the job. If you feel you don't know, do ask. There is a network of services external to the school, e.g. speech therapists, physiotherapists, teacher advisers, educational psychologists and child psychiatrists who can be approached, together with your class teacher, should you want to find out more information. There are also many charitable organisations which offer information about a wide range of disabilities, e.g. The Spastics Society and the Royal National Institute for the Blind. (Appendix B provides more information about the roles of supporting professionals.)

The information contained in the child's school records will give you some background knowledge. You will need to check with the head teacher whether you can have access to this information.

Keeping confidences

This follows on well from the last point. When you work closely with a child, there are bound to be times when you hear or see information, e.g. about the child's home life, which *must* be kept confidential. This does not apply, however, to disclosure of child abuse, which is information you have a duty to share with the head teacher. In the course of your job, you may find people confiding in you. While you can discuss information with other professionals concerned, please remember that the information you come across in the course of your job is not for discussion or comment with outsiders.

Being 'in tune' with the child's physical needs

This refers to the physical well-being of the child. There are occasions when a child comes to school feeling tired, hungry or just not well. This is particularly the case with pupils who have physical disabilities and who may have had disturbed sleep. Children from non-nurturing homes are also at risk. When working with such children, the session is not likely to be an academic success. Don't feel you have failed if nothing is achieved on paper — quite often showing a genuine interest in the child and lending a sympathetic ear goes a long way towards compensating for what may be lacking in the child's background. Be aware of any moodiness or lethargy and make allowances for it. Imagine how you feel yourself when you are tired or run-down, and treat the child with gentleness and sensitivity.

How can I support the teacher?

SNAs identified the following aspects of their supportive role in respect of the class teacher:

- working in partnership

- providing feedback about the pupil
- helping in setting targets, monitoring and evaluating programmes
- recording information
- maintaining a sense of humour.

Working in partnership

Working in any partnership implies COMMUNICATION. In order to work well with a class teacher you must feel able to ask questions, clarify expectations and get feedback on your work with the pupil. It is a two-way process and obviously much depends on the personality and organisational skills of the teacher, on whom you are dependent for direction and guidance.

However, if you are to work effectively it is vital that you meet regularly for information exchange, joint planning and evaluation. In a primary school it need only be for a short time each day or each week but it is in the best interests of the pupils that you do this. In a secondary school this is more difficult as you may be supporting the pupil in up to ten curriculum areas. You may find it more practical to have one longer planning session per month. Planning does take some time commitment by the class teacher but you will be better able to support him or her if you are both clear about what you are both doing.

To quote from the recent Audit Commission/HMI handbook:

> 'Where extra help is provided, planning and communication are the keys to improving its impact.'

This document also stresses the need for the supporting adult to

> '. . . be aware of the class teacher's objectives for a piece of work so that he or she can then focus on what the child is to master, and consider alternative means of reaching the same goal.'

Working in partnership can be a problem, particularly for SNAs who work in secondary schools who will have to work with a number of different teachers. Some staff may have subject specialisms and it may be sometimes necessary for you to ensure that a member of staff understands the way in which you can assist a pupil in a given situation and the limitations of that pupil.

A small minority of teachers feel threatened by the presence of another adult in the classroom. If you feel uncomfortable about any situation it may help to discuss your concerns with the special needs co-ordinator and the teacher concerned. But do remember that your main role is not to give 'marks out of ten' for the quality of any lesson or any teaching style, but to act in the best interests of the pupils who you are employed to support and enable them to make the best of any teaching situation.

Providing feedback about the pupil

In working closely with a particular pupil or group of pupils, it is likely that you will be more sensitive to their needs and reactions in any given situation than is the class teacher, who takes a wider view.

You will be able, therefore, to provide information to the teacher about how well the pupil is coping with the demands made on him or her. This may involve written feedback or record keeping. If a task given to the pupil is too difficult, please don't feel you must persevere with it to the bitter end but feedback to the teacher that this is the case and either get the teacher to modify the task or agree that you yourself can do this. Special needs assistants are often wonderfully creative given the opportunity, so feel confident in making suggestions and modifications as you feel necessary. The majority of teachers will be only too pleased to hear your ideas and take them on board if possible.

"So I thought if I brought some rope I could help Andrew make a bridge. He likes construction activities."

In addition to feedback about how the pupil is coping with school work you will also be able to provide information about the general well being of the pupil and about situations out of school or in the playground which may be affecting the pupil's performance in class.

Helping in setting targets, monitoring and evaluating programmes

In an ideal situation, when you are meeting regularly with the class teacher or special needs co-ordinator, you will be able to make a contribution to the planning of individual programmes (see Chapter 2). It is the responsibility of the class teacher and possibly the special needs co-ordinator to do this for each pupil with special needs, so they might be deciding exactly *what* is the next step for the pupil. You will be able to contribute ideas about *how* this might be done, bearing in mind the temperament of the pupil.

It is also extremely valuable to EVALUATE what you are doing with the pupil. This means 'taking a step back' periodically, say every half term, and asking yourself just how effective your work with the pupil has been and whether the targets or goals set have been achieved. If not, or only partially, it would be worth discussing alternative approaches with the class teacher in order to see if this makes a difference.

But do remember that most children with special needs often learn only slowly and so realistic expectations are clearly needed.

"And I'm hoping that he'll have cracked long division of decimals by the end of next week."

Recording information

As part of your work in supporting the teacher, it is essential that you record what you do in the course of your work with the pupils. The class teacher or special needs co-ordinator will be able to advise you about the sort of records you should keep and the format this should take. The information you will be asked to record will depend on the particular needs of the pupil. For instance, you may be asked to record details about the language the child uses or about how many times he or she shows aggressive behaviour. Whatever the record is, it should contain useful information to help in planning future work rather than just a diary of events. So it might, therefore, be useful to record the date, the activity and the materials used, bearing in mind why you are doing the task. It would then be useful to record an evaluative comment about how well the pupil succeeded in the task.

Consider:

(i) Has the pupil learned?
If not, why not? (task too hard, wrong time of day, too many distractions, unmotivating materials, etc.)
(ii) How might this be done better next time? (discuss with teacher)

Maintaining a sense of humour

When a teacher has a pupil or pupils with special needs in his or her class it can sometimes become hard work as progress is often slow and the level of attention demanded by these pupils is often high. For the health and sanity of the teacher, the pupil and yourself it is a good thing to smile and joke about situations which invite it. Do not allow situations to become too 'heavy' - having a sense of optimism and good humour can help the teacher and the pupils enormously. The old adage 'A burden shared is a burden halved' can be quite true when pupils' difficulties are considered. Mutual support of teacher and special needs assistant can be of tremendous benefit.

Suggestion to enhance mutual support

Take some time to sit down with the teacher(s) you work with and do the following exercise:

(1) I am a special needs assistant. How can I best support the teacher?
(2) I am a teacher. How can I best support the special needs assistant?

How can I support the school?

SNAs identified the following aspects of their supportive role within the school:

- Working as part of the special needs 'team'
- Working with parents
- Contributing to reviews

- Knowing the school procedures
- Attending relevant in-service training or staff meetings
- By using particular personal strengths.

By working as part of the special needs 'team'

Within the school this team will consist of the class teacher(s), the special needs assistant(s) and the special needs co-ordinator, who has a general overview of all pupils in the school who have special educational needs. In secondary schools the year head and class tutor may also have a role. The headteacher has overall responsibility for you and may take an active interest, but usually the role of supervision is delegated to the special needs co-ordinator or class teacher.

There are other professionals whose workbase is outside the school but who come into school regularly to give advice about pupils with special needs and are therefore part of a wider support network. These include educational psychologists, physiotherapists, speech and language therapists and advisory teachers. These people will be pleased to discuss with you any relevant issues related to your work. (See Appendix B.)

In an ideal situation, you will feel valued and supported if colleagues in the school see you as part of a team. Giving you the opportunity to be involved in planning and decision making will encourage your own ideas and creativity and you will feel more positive about your role in the school. This depends largely on the attitudes of other members of staff, some of whom may find partnership working too threatening and are thus unable to treat you as having a different but equal contribution to make. More usually, however, it is because staff are too busy to step back from their daily work and plan ahead with you. Too often, special needs assistants are placed in a 'reactive' role - responding to whatever comes up at the time without any planning, rather than a 'proactive' role - taking time to plan intervention in advance.

In order to make the best use of your time, a teamwork approach is vital. Very few teachers would disagree with this. If you feel you are a 'reactive' SNA then discuss with the class teacher and/or special needs co-ordinator any ideas you might have about improving how your time is used and how you feel the need to be part of a team.

The parents or home carers of the pupils concerned also play a part in this teamwork approach. It is important that they are made aware of the programmes and plans which are being made for their children so that they can be encouraged to support the work of the school at home in whatever way is appropriate. The most important adults in a child's life are the parents and their influence on the child is enormous. It is important that they understand the implications of any difficulty and are helped to be positive in their attitudes and expectations.

Working with parents or carers

Your job may bring you into frequent contact with the child's parents or carers, particularly if the child has physical disabilities. In some cases an important part of your role may be to develop a positive relationship with the parents and to foster links between home and school, working in partnership with the class teacher. At times, it may be necessary to provide a 'listening ear' in order to support the parents and to understand what is going on in the child's home life. It is necessary to keep a safe distance emotionally when this happens and to beware of getting embroiled in complex family dynamics. It is also necessary to keep confidences which may be shared. The class teacher should be aware of relevant issues and should be able to intervene should things become too 'heavy'. Sometimes it is very hard for parents to accept that their child has a special need. You may have a part to play in helping them to come to terms with this and to be realistic. Valuing what a child is good at and pointing out progress, may be part of your role in such a situation.

Contributing to reviews

Every pupil who has a statement of special educational needs must have a review of their special educational needs, at least annually. This includes a meeting when all concerned with the pupil, both inside the school and outside, can come together, discuss recent reports, inform each other about progress and make plans for meeting the pupil's needs in the future. Pupils without statements may also have internal review meetings.

If you have had close contact with the pupil, you may be asked to give a short verbal or written report at the meeting and if you have kept records they will prove useful in giving your report. Do remember that there will always be people within the school who will help you to do this and opportunities for you to discuss your contribution before the meeting.

"Ahem! Friends, parents and countrymen . . ."

Occasionally there will be case conferences about children with whom you are involved. Such meetings normally follow a pupil's exclusion from school or some concern voiced by the health department or social services. Again you may be asked to give your perspective about the pupil's needs. On rare occasions, you could be asked to give your views on a child's needs and progress for court hearings.

Knowing the school procedures

You will be able to support the school effectively if you make sure you know about school policies and procedures, e.g. accidents;

discipline; bullying; out of school visits; child protection etc. Ask the headteacher what procedures you need to know of if you are unsure.

There will also be ongoing procedural changes. It is unlikely that you will attend all staff meetings (which are normally held outside the SNA contracted hours) so in order to be aware of week-by-week changes, you need to refer to a member of staff, probably the special needs co-ordinator, who should make you aware of changes, particularly if they affect you. Again COMMUNICATION is the key factor.

"Sorry, did no-one tell you the trip's been postponed until next week?"

Attending relevant in-service training or staff meetings

When opportunities arise to further your knowledge about special needs or to be involved in meetings about whole school initiatives, then do try to attend. Ideally, this time should come from within your school hours - in reality many SNAs choose to work additional hours in order that their pupils do not miss out.

At present, training courses for special needs assistants are few and far between. This need for training is now being recognised, and provided for (e.g. the City and Guilds 'Certificate in Learning Support' is now an option in Hampshire through the collaboration of the local authority educational psychology and special needs support services with a local FE college.)

By using particular personal strengths

The whole class, and maybe the school, can benefit if you are prepared to share any particular talent you might have. It could be that you are a good singer or can play an instrument well. Perhaps you have artistic or dramatic talent or maybe your culinary or D.I.Y. skills are renowned. Don't hide your light under a bushel - be willing to contribute. And don't underestimate the parenting skills you may have - the vast majority of SNAs are parents themselves so can often provide insights about what might be appropriate to solve common childhood problems.

"Don't hide your light under a bushel!"

What makes an effective special needs assistant?

The following qualities were described by a group of Special Needs Assistants.

- patience
- care
- sense of fairness
- consistency
- sensitivity
- ability to learn from mistakes
- flexibility
- versatility
- positive attitudes
- friendly
- hard to shock
- sense of humour
- enthusiasm

Most SNAs possess many of these qualities and become aware of areas which need to be worked on.

"Saint or superwoman? — or both!"

CHAPTER 4

The role of the teacher in working with the special needs assistant

The class teacher has a key role to play in managing special needs assistance. In using this type of classroom support it is helpful to consider the following aspects of the teacher's role:

- supporting the special needs assistant
- making effective use of special needs assistance.

How can the class teacher support the SNA?

Eighty teachers who work in partnership with special needs assistants were asked to define their supporting role (SNA in-service training courses 1991 and 1992, Certificate in Learning Support, Hampshire). Their responses can be summarised under the following headings:

- ensuring the SNA is clear about the roles and responsibilities of the job;
- providing regular opportunities for planning and discussion;
- encouraging the work of the SNA and providing positive feedback;
- making sure the SNA knows the learning implications of the pupil's special need;
- making clear and realistic requests;
- valuing the SNA as part of the special needs 'team';
- providing training opportunities for the special needs assistant.

Ensuring that the special needs assistant is clear about the roles and responsibilities of the job

When teachers start their first teaching appointment, it is after considerable time has been spent in training and teaching practice.

Please remember that the majority of SNAs have not had any training and their experience of school life may well be limited to their own schooldays. So a special needs assistant who is new to the job will need a period of induction when such mysteries as the National Curriculum, Child Protection legislation, Records of Achievement and school policy and routines can be explained. In addition the job description (see Appendix A) can be further clarified and ground-rules for working established (see: 'What are the ground rules?' Chapter 2).

Providing regular opportunities for planning and discussion

The importance of regular meetings for planning, monitoring and evaluating the work of the SNA is vital and is the key to ensuring a high quality school experience for the pupil with special needs. This aspect of partnership working is addressed in detail in the next section ('How can teachers make effective use of special needs assistance?').

Encouraging the work of the SNA and providing positive feedback

Most SNAs, particularly when new to the role, admit to feeling under-confident about their work. This is usually because they have been away from the workplace for some time and also because they have had no training about what to expect, either in terms of the role they will fulfil or about the special needs they will meet. Encouragement from teachers is important in order to build confidence. Positive feedback about what has worked well and constructive criticism provided as 'improvement suggestions' can work wonders in transforming dispirited SNAs into enthusiastic and confident colleagues.

Making sure the SNA knows the learning implications of the pupil's special need

Each type of special need has associated implications for learning (see Chapter 5, 'What special needs will I meet?'). It is important that the teacher explains these implications to the special needs assistant so that realistic outcomes can be expected from the learning tasks. For instance, a pupil with emotional problems may achieve very little academically on some days. On such occasions a 'listening ear' may do much more in supporting the pupil than will insistence on the completion of a page of writing.

Knowing the learning implications entails providing work for the pupil at the right level so that success is likely. It is important that the teacher makes clear to the SNA just what the purpose of the learning task is so that alternatives can be considered if necessary.

Making clear and realistic requests

When asked about issues which prevent effective partnership working, SNAs report that they are sometimes asked to do tasks which they feel they cannot do, either because they are unclear about the task or because they feel they do not have the expertise (Information from SNAs, Certificate in Learning Support, S.W. Hampshire, 1992). As a teacher, therefore, do not assume that the SNA has psychic powers but make requests clear, checking out that the SNA has understood. Remember that it is the responsibility of the teacher to decide the teaching methods, the materials to be used and the recording system. It is also the responsibility of the teacher to manage and monitor the work of the SNA in supporting pupils with special needs. This can only be done effectively if communication is clear and realistic and if the SNA is not overburdened with responsibilities which clearly belong with the teacher.

Valuing the SNA as part of the special needs 'team'

It is important that the special needs assistant is encouraged to see herself as part of a 'team' in supporting pupils with special needs. The class teacher can encourage this perception by valuing the views of the assistant and ensuring that the perspective of the SNA is shared whenever there is a full case discussion about the pupil. This may be as part of the Annual Review process or at a case conference. The class teacher has a role in encouraging other members of staff and also the parents to have a positive view of the special needs assistant as a colleague who works in partnership with teachers and parents to meet children's needs.

Providing training opportunities for the special needs assistant

(see also 'The need for training' Chapter 6)

In an effective working partnership, the teacher will take every opportunity to develop the knowledge and skills of the special needs assistant within the normal working environment and in regular meetings. It is also very helpful to the development of the SNA if she can be encouraged to attend any relevant in-service training courses. It can also be useful for assistants to visit other schools in order to observe good practice and discuss common issues with other SNAs. This is particularly helpful in a school which has only one or two SNAs, when sometimes the role can seem like a lonely one.

As part of the work done with class teachers and special needs assistants in Hampshire (Certificate of Learning Support), twelve competencies have been recognised as those skills which special needs assistants need to develop. As a class teacher it may be useful to consider whether you can help the assistant you work with to develop or further improve in any of these skills, as part of your role in training. The competencies are as follows:

Supporting and Relating

- is capable of establishing and developing appropriate relationships with adults and children;
- demonstrates teamwork skills (collaboration, liaison);
- demonstrates ability to listen;
- offers encouragement;
- shows awareness of pupils' needs;
- seeks clarification.

Facilitating the Learning Process

- shows awareness of the range of special needs (learning and behaviour);
- has an awareness of the processes of learning;
- has some knowledge of child development;
- demonstrates self-evaluation;
- can give clear instructions.

Understanding the Planning and Managing Process

- is aware of goals that have been set;
- records work accurately;
- understands the nature and role of support services;
- understands school structures and procedures.

How can teachers make effective use of special needs assistance?

In 1992, a report by the Audit Commission/HMI was published, entitled *Getting in on the Act*. This report described the provision made by schools and LEAs in England and Wales for pupils with special educational needs and made recommendations for action at national and local levels to improve the effectiveness of this service. The management handbook *Getting the Act Together* was published as a companion volume. This document provides detailed guidance for schools and LEAs and in it there is a section about managing extra adults in the classroom. There are a number of action points recommended to schools and teachers within this section of the handbook. The main recommendation is:

> '*Schools and teachers should plan the use of extra adult support for pupils with special needs* - Where extra adult help is provided, planning and communication are the keys to improving its impact.'

Advice to teachers

Three action points are recommended to teachers:

1. *'Teacher and supporting adult have agreed in which lessons there is a role for the latter.'*

You should decide in which lessons the SNA really needs to be giving support to the pupil and in which lessons he or she might usefully be employed elsewhere. To quote from the handbook:

> '. . . it is not uncommon for a supporting adult to sit through a lesson with virtually no useful role because the style of the lesson precludes working with individual pupils. Examples of this are class discussions and use of audio- visual resources. With a degree of planning, the supporting adult need not spend the whole time in the lesson.'

An instance is described in which a supporting adult for a child with visual impairment was not in the classroom, but usefully preparing braille worksheets elsewhere, once it had been checked that the pupil could manage in this lesson without support - and this was a practical science lesson! Common sense is clearly needed in negotiating the best use of special needs assistance.

It is good practice for the SNA to work with the pupil in the mainstream classroom whenever possible. Consideration should be given as to whether the SNA should work alongside the pupil, with a small group of pupils or at a distance observing when the pupil needs support, and moving in only at those times. The SNA should be encouraged to promote the independence of the pupil at every possible opportunity.

2. *'Role of the supporting adult has been planned'*

It is essential that the teacher spends time clarifying relative roles and responsibilities (see Chapter 2 - The Role of the Special Needs Assistant). It is clear from the work done with SNAs and teachers that time spent in planning is time very well spent. 'If a small amount of the time currently spent alongside pupils were redirected into planning and discussion about individual pupils between support and classroom teachers, there would be a significant improvement in effectiveness.' Moreover, both teacher and SNA would feel better about their work with pupils with special needs and the pupils will reap the benefits of partnership working.

3. *'Teacher or supporting adult prepare special materials if necessary. To increase pupils' independence, consideration is given to preparing special lesson materials as well as providing side-by-side support.'*

It is likely that the pupil or pupils supported by a special needs assistant will need worksheets and activities which are modified in some way so that he or she can understand the instructions and complete the task with some degree of success. This is particularly the case if the pupil has learning difficulties. Given clear directions by the teacher, the special needs assistant can be of great help in providing these special materials. This point recognises the importance of allowing the pupil to work independently rather than having an assistant sitting alongside all the time. A 'beneficial circle' is described, in which '. . . professional time is used to modify resources which enable the pupil to exercise more independence, thus freeing further professional time.'

Advice to schools

Two action points are recommended to schools about managing extra adults in the classroom.

1. *'Time is allocated for communication between teacher and supporting adult.'*

Discussions with both teachers and special needs assistants highlight the importance of time spent together in order to plan, monitor and evaluate individual pupil programmes (see Chapter 2, 'What is the individual programme for the pupil?'). These meetings should be on at least a weekly basis and, in some cases, on a daily basis. If, as a teacher, you feel that not enough or even no time is allocated for this purpose, then it is clearly an issue which you should be addressing with the head teacher and with the other members of staff in your school.

2. *'School managers observe impact of extra adults in classroom on pupils with special needs.'*

A special needs assistant is an expensive human resource which, if used to best effect, can make a significant difference to the school experience of a pupil with a special need. However, if the use of the SNA is not clearly thought out it can sometimes have detrimental effects on the pupil, through no fault of the SNA e.g. a pupil recently transferred from a special school to a mainstream secondary school with the resource of ten hours special needs assistance remarked 'It's brilliant here, but there's a lady who keeps following me around and I'm not stupid - I want to do it on my own!' Clearly there is a need for school managers to plan and monitor the use of assistance, taking into account the perceptions of the pupil, so that the support is used in a sensitive and meaningful way. The book by Margaret Balshaw entitled *Help in the Classroom* gives useful advice and provides workshop materials for schools to use in order to improve their policies and practice in using assistance.

CHAPTER 5

What special needs will I meet?

Learning difficulties

The majority of pupils who have special educational needs will have learning difficulties. Some will have learning difficulties as a result of physical disability or sensory impairment. Some of these pupils may have normal intellectual ability and potential but need to access learning opportunities through the use of special equipment, supervision or simply 'an extra pair of hands' (the term 'supervision', as used here, relates to safety as well as support). Other pupils will have particular learning difficulties associated with their disability.

Before considering the effects of special educational need and learning difficulty it is important for all adults who work with children to understand the ways in which *all* children learn. Here are some fundamental statements about learning (Hampshire Inspection and Advisory Support Service, 1992).

It is important to view learning difficulties as a *relative* term. Remember:

> 'If the tasks and activities in which the learner is engaged are not matched to the learner's capabilities, or are not understood by the learner, then learning difficulties are likely to occur.'
>
> (Ainscow and Tweddle)

The importance of matching the task to the child is made very clear in the 1981 Act. This stresses that 'special educational needs' is a relative term which arises from the interaction between a child and his or her environment. Teachers and SNAs should be working together to predict potential pitfalls for the child. By planning realistic and achievable learning tasks, learning difficulties can be avoided.

As a special needs assistant you should see your role as 'prevention rather than cure' whenever possible.

As an assistant in the classroom you may find there are certain tensions caused because those who are directing your work are unsure about your role in supporting pupils with special needs. Teachers, as well as assistants need to be clear about the reasons for support and clear about *how* support can best be used.

Some of these tensions arise because teachers feel that some children lack certain skills and the role of the assistant is therefore to bridge the gap and compensate for what is considered to be missing.

WAYS IN WHICH CHILDREN LEARN

1. CHILDREN LEARN PRIMARILY THROUGH PRACTICAL AND FIRST-HAND EXPERIENCES.

2. CHILDREN LEARN THROUGH ALL THEIR SENSES.

3. CHILDREN MAKE SENSE OF NEW EXPERIENCES BY RELATING THEM TO PREVIOUS LEARNING.

4. CHILDREN DEVELOP THEIR UNDERSTANDING THROUGH TALKING.

5. CHILDREN HAVE DIFFERENT PREFERRED LEARNING STYLES AND LEARN AT DIFFERENT RATES.

6. CHILDREN MAY MOVE ACROSS SUBJECT BOUNDARIES AS THEY LEARN.

7. CHILDREN LEARN BEST WHEN THEY CAN MAKE SENSE OF WHAT THEY DO THROUGH INVOLVEMENT IN PLANNING AND REFLECTION.

8. CHILDREN LEARN THROUGH PURPOSEFUL REPETITION, PRACTICE AND RE-INFORCEMENT.

9. CHILDREN LEARN BEST WHEN THERE IS CARE, TOLERANCE, SECURITY, PRAISE AND HIGH EXPECTATIONS, ASSOCIATED WITH CLEAR LEARNING GOALS.

This idea about special needs being 'normality minus some bits' is not helpful or healthy in considering the child as this idea often filters through to the child, making him or her feel different. It is far better for teachers and assistants to encourage the pupil to feel that he or she can succeed in whatever task is being tried. This means providing a task *at the right level* so that success is assured.

Difficulties for the pupil arise when the demands put on him or her are too great, e.g.

1. the pupil is given a worksheet of multiplication tables when he is still working on addition;
2. the pupil is expected to stay in his seat for a full hour, when normally he can only manage five minutes.

It is like being told to sit with knitting needles and wool and follow a complex knitting pattern when you have only just mastered knit one purl one! When this happens the normal reaction is to give up on the task and feel a failure.

The key to success is clear - we need to provide tasks at the right level for the pupil. This is an important concept for all adults who work with children.

Pupils who need additional support to enable them to learn effectively have the following needs:

• learning tasks and activities should be matched to the ability of the child;
• learning should be planned in small steps with frequent repetition - go over what has been taught often so that the child does not forget;
• more adult guidance and reassurance is required - give plenty of encouragement;
• realistic objectives should be set - be clear about the capabilities of the child and don't expect too much - or too little!
• a wide variety of materials and opportunity to learn through first-hand experiences is necessary.

There are different kinds of special educational need, some of which may result in learning difficulties. These difficulties are usually described as follows.

Mild Learning Difficulties

It has been estimated that there are 18 per cent of all pupils who will have some kind of mild learning difficulty at some time during their school life. These pupils are unlikely to have a statement of special educational need. Special needs assistants are frequently called upon to support such pupils whose mild special needs may be described as follows:-

• mild conductive hearing loss (e.g. 'glue ear')
• slight physical disability (e.g. mild cerebral palsy)
• poor eye/hand co-ordination
• clumsiness
• hyperactivity
• slow to develop reading and writing skills
• general immaturity
• poor vocabulary
• slow to understand new ideas
• short concentration span/distractibility

These pupils should not need a high level of support but attention needs to be given to particular areas of need with the possibility of including a structured activity to meet the particular need.

The vast majority of children who have mild learning difficulties lack self-confidence in their learning ability. Please remember to take every opportunity to enable the child to succeed and be ready to give praise and encouragement for small amounts of progress. What appears to be a small step may be a giant leap for the child.

Moderate Learning Difficulties (mld)

Pupils identified as having moderate learning difficulties are those pupils who have limited ability in both verbal and non-verbal skills. They are pupils who learn at a slower pace than do other boys and girls of the same age.

It used to be the case that these children were educated in special schools. Since the 1981 Education Act and its emphasis on children being educated in the mainstream where possible, increasing numbers of 'mld' pupils have their needs met in ordinary schools, usually with additional teacher support and/or special needs assistance. The main indicator of whether this is in the best interests of the pupil is the ability of the pupil to cope with the social and emotional demands of a mainstream school setting, and the ability of the mainstream school to provide an appropriate curriculum. There remain a number of 'mld' pupils who require the more sheltered and nurturing support which special schools offer and who would flounder and fail to thrive in a mainstream setting.

Pupils who have moderate learning difficulties often have the following associated problems:

- poor memory
- short attention span
- low interest in academic subjects
- limited ability to apply learning in one situation to another situation (generalisation)
- inability to understand abstract ideas

If you are working with a child who has moderate learning difficulties, please remember:

- *He or she needs practical work in order to learn* ('active learning').

Every opportunity for using visual aids and practical apparatus should be used.

- *Overlearning is necessary*

Frequent repetition and practice of skills acquired is important in order to reinforce learning

- *Language work is essential*

Vocabulary and language use is likely to be poor, so regular activities which broaden vocabulary and increase understanding of language are essential

- *Confidence building is crucial*

Children who have moderate learning difficulties often have low self-esteem and perceive themselves as failures, so take every opportunity to give praise and build confidence.

Severe Learning Difficulties (sld)

Pupils identified as having severe learning difficulties usually are those pupils who have very limited general ability and who learn at a much slower pace than do other boys and girls of the same age. These learning difficulties are often because these children are genetically different from most other children (e.g. Down's syndrome) or because of medical trauma (e.g. brain damage as a result of tumour or oxygen deprivation at birth).

Most of these pupils are educated in special schools although some are wholly or partially integrated in mainstream schools.

Pupils who are identified as having severe learning difficulties have similar characteristics to those with moderate difficulties but they frequently need a higher level of adult support and learn at a slower rate. Even as adults, they may be unable to cope independently without the support of caring adults. It is therefore necessary to teach life-skills (e.g. shopping, cooking) to these pupils as a priority, particularly as they get older. The younger child will take longer to learn 'self-help' skills (e.g. feeding, use of toilet) and your help is likely to be needed in these areas.

If you are working with a child who has severe learning difficulties, please remember:

• *Slow progress is likely*
Progress may be slow but the children can and do learn given consistent support at the right level.
• *Practical experiences are vital*
The need for 'first-hand' experience is clear (e.g. shopping trips to learn about the use of money).
• *Language work is essential*
Encouraging understanding of language and use of language is very important in the learning process.
• *Allow the pupil to choose*
Try to provide the pupil with opportunities to make choices, as it is by developing the ability to choose that control over the environment is developed. Don't let the pupil become too dependent on you!

Profound and Multiple Learning Difficulties (pmld)

Pupils described as having profound and multiple learning difficulties have both severe physical disabilities and severe learning difficulties. They may also have sensory disability (hearing and sight). These children often have limited understanding of language and little or no speech, so communication is often difficult.

When working with these children, who are mainly in special schools, the first priority must be their physical comfort. There will be many routine tasks (e.g. feeding, dressing, toileting) which these children cannot do for themselves and your help will be required. In order to assist with some of these tasks you will need clear directions on how to move pupils from one place to another, for both their benefit and your own. Backache is a common complaint among adults who work with children. Do ask about how you can avoid this and learn the correct techniques for lifting and moving children.

Once the child is comfortable, the priorities then become educational. Establishing some means of communication is of key importance. This may be through visual contact, through touch, through sounds, through taste and smell, i.e. working through all the senses.

If you are working with a child who has profound and multiple learning difficulties, please remember:

• These children can and do learn although progress is often very slow. Have positive expectations.
• Give encouragement and praise even though you may be unsure of whether the child understands. Assume that he or she does! If you

seem to get no response, it may be because the child cannot physically make the response - there may be an emotional response which you cannot see.

• In some cases, children will actually regress as a result of medical factors and occasionally a child may die. Be aware that this is a possibility.

Specific Learning Difficulties (spld) (also called Dyslexia)

Pupils described as having specific learning difficulties have normal general ability but poor literacy skills (reading, spelling, writing) and sometimes poor numeracy skills. There is a mis-match between the pupil's ability to understand and answer questions verbally, which is good, and the ability of the pupil to read, spell or write, which is poor. These sorts of problems are sometimes referred to as dyslexic difficulties. A significant number of children have specific learning difficulties which are relatively mild and more boys than girls are affected. A small number (maybe one or two in each school) have quite marked difficulties requiring a high level of support.

These pupils usually have limited ability to remember letter shape and sequence. They can benefit from what is known as a 'multi-sensory' approach to learning. This means using visual, auditory and kinaesthetic (movement) strategies or clues to help them learn and remember which letter sounds and letter shapes go together.

If you are working with children who have specific learning difficulties, please remember:

• Find out what the child is good at and make sure those skills are valued. Pupils who have specific learning difficulties frequently experience feelings of frustration and loss of confidence so it is important that self-esteem is boosted.

• The child is not being lazy if he or she seems to have forgotten all the work done at the last session (or even five minutes ago!). Strategies for remembering sequences and written information are poor so daily activities to improve memory can be of great value.

Emotional and Behavioural Difficulties (ebd)

Emotional and Behavioural Difficulties is a blanket term which includes a very wide range of conditions - perhaps the only characteristic these share in common is that the children experiencing them are both troubled and troubling to those who come into contact with them.

The emotional difficulties which lead to interpersonal and social problems range from, on the one hand, 'internalising' behaviour, e.g. withdrawal/shyness, depression, extreme anxiety and compulsions; to 'acting out' behaviours (sometimes called conduct disorders) e.g. extreme aggression (to people or property), anti-social behaviour, bullying, defiance.

If a child receives inadequate emotional nurturing from the parents or carers, particularly at an early age, then the likelihood of emotional and behavioural difficulties is high. Physical and sexual abuse also increase the likelihood of emotional and behavioural difficulties. Learning difficulties can also cause emotional problems for children. A sensitive educational environment and curriculum at the right level is necessary.

There are many factors which indicate difficulties of this kind and the vast majority of children, at some point in their school lives, will have some emotional and behavioural problems - indeed it is part of normal development. Children with special needs of any kind experience these difficulties as part of their perception of themselves as being 'different'. However, it is when problems persist over a long period of time and become severe and complex, that additional support will be necessary.

Pupils experiencing severe emotional and behavioural difficulties may need special provision where small class groups and a high level of adult attention is offered. There are many pupils in our mainstream schools who also show these difficulties and schools report increasing numbers of such pupils. Special needs assistants play a significant part in supporting them and making it possible for them to remain in their local schools. The majority of these children do not achieve what they are capable of in academic subjects at school because no child can learn effectively if he or she is troubled inside and has feelings of worthlessness.

If you are working with a pupil who has emotional and behavioural difficulties, please remember:

• *Take every opportunity to improve the self-esteem of the pupil*
Give praise when they conform to normally expected standards of behaviour in school or when they have achieved something they have never done before. This can be related to school work or to behaviour. Try to 'catch them being good' and let them know why you are pleased.

> 'Gemma, I like the way you came into the classroom this morning.'
> (behaviour)
> 'Robert, you've read those words really well today. Well done!'
> (school work)

• *Rewards are very important*
This shows the child when he or she is succeeding and that it is worthwhile to succeed! Find out what your child values as a reward. Sometimes a word of praise or a pat on the back can be enough but for many children described as having emotional and behavioural difficulties this will not be enough and you will need to provide more tangible rewards (a wall chart with targets, a favourite game etc.).

• *Develop your listening skills* (see 'Supporting the pupil', Chapter 3)
You will be sensitive to the feelings of the pupil if you can listen and observe effectively. If you can encourage the pupil to talk about feelings, it can be helpful. Try to look for solutions to the problems rather than dwelling on the causes. (Ask 'What needs to happen in order to avoid this situation in the future?') There will be many parts

of the pupil's life which you cannot change for the better. Accept this and concentrate on those parts you can change (e.g. self-esteem, patterns of behaviour in school).

• *Encourage the pupil to take responsibility*

Many pupils with emotional and behavioural difficulties find it very hard to take responsibility for their own actions. Enabling them to understand what effects their behaviour has on others is an important step in moving towards changing unhelpful behaviour patterns. Role play or drama activities can be very helpful to these pupils in enabling them to do this.

If you can give the pupil a position of responsibility in the group then this will also assist the development of mutual support and social responsibility and it will also foster a sense of trust.

• *Point out good role models*

Do not assume that the child knows how to behave. You may need to teach him or her the behaviours which are needed in school. If you can demonstrate yourself what is wanted or get the child to copy another child who is behaving well then you will be demonstrating what is expected. Do not overdo this however - it can be very bad for self-esteem if it is always being pointed out that others do it right!

• *Try to anticipate trouble*

Learn to recognise those situations in which problems for the pupil commonly arise, e.g. lining up at the door, coming in from break, being late to lessons. Help the pupil to recognise these situations for himself or herself and work out strategies for minimising or avoiding trouble. If a pupil can learn to keep out of the way of other pupils who seek confrontation, then this can make a tremendous difference to his or her life in school.

• *Deal with 'bad' behaviour in a positive way*

By the very nature of their difficulties, these children will not always behave like the majority of the others. This is to be expected. However, when incidents or confrontations do occur, it is important to deal with them in a calm and reasonable way. Remember to label the behaviour and not the child. Calling a child 'stupid', 'naughty', 'bully' or 'slow' only serves to re-inforce the idea in the child's mind that they are indeed 'stupid', 'naughty', 'bully' or 'slow'. The message must be 'I like you but I don't like your behaviour'. It is often helpful to talk about the effects the behaviour has had and the feelings it engenders in others.

> 'Jane, when you take money from the teacher's drawer it lets me down, and I'm sad about that because I want to trust you.'

Communicating your own feelings about the incident can be helpful.

> 'John, I feel angry when you mess about because you don't give me your best work and I know you can do better than this.'

Staying calm is very important. If you 'lose your cool' it will only serve to make the pupil feel worse and increase the likelihood of the incident occuring again.

• *Be realistic*
Be realistic in setting goals for the pupil. Don't try to change all 'bad' behaviour at once. Choose one objective to start with (e.g. sitting in seat for five minutes, not shouting out for ten minutes). Be consistent, make it clear to the pupil what you are aiming for and reward the pupil if the target is achieved. Remember that it took a long time for the pupil to learn their patterns of behaviour, and overnight transformations are unlikely.

Helpful information and workshop activities for improving self-esteem in children can be found in a video workshop pack 'A Bag of Tricks' (Barbara Maines and George Robinson). There is a useful booklet to accompany the course *You Can - You Know You Can* (Lame Duck Publications). This may be accessible through the school's educational psychologist.

Physical Disability

The term 'physical disability' covers a wide range of conditions. The more common ones you are likely to come across include:

- cerebral palsy
- spina bifida
- hydrocephalus
- cystic fibrosis
- muscular dystrophy
- diabetes
- epilepsy
- haemophilia
- limb deficiency
- asthma
- brittle bone disease
- eczema

Within each category, the effects of the disability range from the relatively minor, so that the child can lead a 'normal' independent life, to relatively severe, so that the child cannot function without the support of caring adults.

Until quite recently, pupils with physical disabilities attended special schools but ideas about physical disabilities have changed from the rather negative concept of 'handicap' to the more positive concepts of 'disability' or 'impairment'. The rights of people with disabilities to have access to normal experience has been recognised and the general public is much more aware of people with disabilities and the part they play in community life. Now, whenever possible, these pupils should have their needs met in mainstream schools. There are still considerable numbers of these children whose additional needs are such that special schooling is appropriate at present. These are the ones whose health is often at risk, or who require very specialised equipment or who require daily intensive physiotherapy, i.e. those who would 'fail to thrive' in a mainstream setting either physically or emotionally.

Different disabilities result in different special needs. You will need to ask the teacher you work with about the details of the disability - educational psychologists, teacher advisers and school medical officers (doctors) can also give you details of associated learning difficulties and physical needs. For instance, pupils who have cerebral palsy sometimes have visuo-perceptual difficulties, i.e. they do not perceive visual images in the same way as other children. Pupils with hydrocephalus sometimes have mood swings and times when they feel very tired. Pupils with spina bifida sometimes have poor fine motor control (i.e. poor control of pencil and hand movements).

On the other hand, it is likely that pupils with conditions such as cystic fibrosis, asthma, brittle bone disease may have no learning difficulties as such but they may need a sensitivity to other needs e.g. tiredness, mood swings, and assistance in managing equipment or physiotherapy routines.

One Step Behind

Promoting independence is an essential part of your role with all 'special needs' pupils. It is particularly important for pupils who have physical disabilities. You need to be 'one step behind' rather than 'one step ahead'. This means allowing the pupil to take calculated risks, on occasion - you will need to discuss this with the class teacher, headteacher, teacher adviser and on occasions the school medical officer, and think through the possible consequences!

It is a difficult task to maintain the balance between giving support and promoting independence. This involves you being clear about your expectations and firm in your directions without pressurising the child. However, sensitivity should tell you if and when to intervene.

Self-help

Part of your role may be enabling the child to look after himself or herself and to master those skills which able-bodied children take for granted, e.g. feeding, dressing, going to the toilet. When helping children in these ways it is important to treat them with dignity and respect and to provide privacy when appropriate.

Mobility

Pupils may need aids in the form of wheelchairs, crutches, mechanical limbs or calipers in order to get around. You will need to familiarise yourself with this equipment and make sure the pupil can use it with comfort and control. Most children learn to transfer themselves from place to place when required, e.g. from a wheelchair to the toilet, with little help. Younger children or very disabled pupils may need more help. If you need to assist in moving a child, you must know the correct techniques for lifting in order to avoid injury to either yourself or the child. Ask for support - quite literally! Lifting techniques must be taught, for each child, by a physiotherapist.

When working with a child with a physical disability, please remember:

- Behave towards him or her as you would to any other pupil of the same age.
- Do not do all the talking for the child or answer for him or her. Let the child make the choices. Never talk for the child, except to repeat what has been said if you are sure the child does not understand.

• Make sure you know the implications of the disability (physical, educational and emotional).

Further useful information about supporting children with physical disabilities can be found in a booklet entitled *Working Together Towards Independence* (Fenton).

Sensory Impairment

Sensory impairment, as the name suggests, refers to any impairment of the senses which may prevent normal progress and development. There are two main types, visual impairment (VI) and hearing impairment (HI). Rarely, children will have both.

Visual impairment (VI)

A recent survey by the Royal National Institute for the Blind indicates that in Britain there are approximately 10,000 children aged 2-19 years who have visual impairment as a primary disabling factor. If children with visual impairment and additional special needs (e.g. profound and multiple learning difficulties) are considered, then there are at least double that number.

This survey also showed the increase over recent years in the proportion of VI children who go to mainstream schools, with varying levels of support, a lot of this support coming from special needs assistants together with peripatetic teachers of the visually impaired.

The impairment may be moderate, in which case your work might be mainly concerned with adapting materials and ensuring safety. If the impairment is severe you may need to learn braille and keyboard skills in order to produce materials the child can use and thus learn effectively. You may also need to assist the child in learning how to get around the classroom and the school with safety.

When working with a visually impaired pupil, your responsibilities are likely to be in three main areas:

1. to provide support for the class teacher by adapting teaching materials, e.g. enlarging worksheets, so that the pupil can follow the same programmes of work as the other members of the class;

2. to ensure the safety of the pupil and others, e.g. safe use of science equipment;

3. to support the pupil by helping him or her to learn any special skills, e.g. braille, and to offer support in all areas in which he or she may be disadvantaged. These areas are:

Orientation and mobility
Clear verbal directions are necessary before any task involving physical movement is attempted. The visually impaired child does not have a visual image of what is required so a visual demonstration is a waste of time, e.g. in PE, if the class teacher is demonstrating, you may need to talk through the steps, for instance, 'Move three steps to the right, jump with both feet together, then three steps to the left'.

Games and leisure

It is sometimes difficult for children with sight problems to join in with informal games and conversations. You may be able to help here, by opening up possibilities for your child to join in and become part of the group.

Social skills

The child with a visual impairment has a social communication problem as he or she cannot always see and therefore interpret the intentions of others. A major way in which children learn is through copying other children and adults but a child with a visual impairment may be unable to do this. This means that he or she will be unable to see a great many actions, facial expressions and non-verbal messages and, as a result, may miss out on this type of learning. Don't be offended if these children use the wrong non-verbal messages and be prepared to teach them the acceptable ways of interacting in a group situation (e.g. remind the child to turn his or her face towards you when speaking).

And remember:

Visually impaired children often miss out on ideas and meanings because of limited vision. It is therefore important to use 'hands on' experience whenever possible. e.g. when talking about pigs, give the child a pig to hold or, better still, take the child to a farm and let him or her hear and feel a real pig!

Hearing impairment (HI)

There is a wide range of hearing impairment, from slight to severe, although total lack of hearing is extremely rare. Statistics published by the National Deaf Children's Society estimate that there are 28,000 school aged children with significant hearing impairment. 14 per cent are educated in special schools for the deaf; 15 per cent in units attached to mainstream schools, and 71 per cent are in their local mainstream schools. Many of these children receive support from a peripatetic teacher of the hearing impaired. Special needs assistants support these children by working with the class teacher and following specialist advice which allows the pupil to play as full a part as possible in school life.

Children who have normal hearing skills acquire ideas and concepts about the world around them largely through spoken language. The words we use to describe objects and experiences provide the child with a 'framework' to build on and learn effectively through reasoning and memory skills. For the child with a hearing impairment, understanding of language is limited, so this 'framework' which is vital for learning is incomplete. These children may then appear slow to learn, particularly in language based tasks of speaking, listening, reading, writing. Reasoning and memory skills may also appear to be poor. However, many of these pupils have normal ability and good non-verbal and visual skills. There are many factors which influence whether a hearing impaired child hears and understands speech. These include:

- the kind and degree of hearing loss
- the age at which deafness developed
- the age at which it was discovered
- the issue and proper use of a suitable hearing aid
- early training
- attentiveness of the child. (Bennett)

As a special needs assistant working with the child you may find it helpful to be clear about these factors in the child's background in order to understand the hearing loss and its educational implications. Ask a specialist teacher of the hearing impaired to discuss this with you.

If you support a child with a hearing impairment then you need to appreciate that the child has a *communication* problem and that your first task is to ensure as far as possible that the child is reliably receiving and understanding all communication from staff and pupils and is routinely participating in all class activities. Your role with the child who has a moderate to severe loss might involve ensuring the correct use of any hearing aid equipment provided for the child, and you may also need to learn a signing system if that is advised as appropriate for the child.

Your role with the child who has a hearing loss will involve ensuring that the child is in the best position in the class to hear what the teacher says and checking out with the child, by asking, what they have understood about the task they have to do.

When working with a child with hearing impairment, please remember:

- The sense of hearing is limited so reinforce as much spoken language as possible through the other senses. Use visual aids and tactile (touching) experiences whenever you can. Visual clues through lipreading, signing and gesturing may be necessary to ensure that the child understands. You can be advised about this by a teacher of the hearing impaired.
- Pupils with moderate to severe hearing loss may be unable to acquire the skills of speaking, listening, reading and writing at a normal rate. For these children it is essential to provide individual programmes to focus on the development of these skills. For these children appropriate activities and/or modifications to the curriculum may be advised by a specialist teacher who will discuss your role in implementing these with you and the class teacher.
- Use visual aids and real experiences whenever you can.
- Communicating with others is a basic need. Pupils with hearing impairment may feel frustrated about their inability to communicate and so may lack self-esteem and occasionally become aggressive. You will need to establish communication with the child yourself, and help others do so. You may also need to be particularly sensitive to the child's emotional needs.

Language impairment

It has been estimated that there are approximately 250,000 children under five and the same number between 5 - 16 in England and Wales who have language impairment. Some are in special schools but the majority attend mainstream schools (figures from the Association For All Speech Impaired Children, AFASIC). If identified at a pre-school level, these children receive support from speech therapy services and a fortunate few attend specialised nurseries. For some children appropriate support in those vital early years is enough to enable them to overcome their difficulties but others go into school with an 'invisible' disability and require ongoing support from teachers, speech and language therapists and special needs assistants. Often the role of the SNA is to work with the child to follow an individual programme which is monitored by the speech and language therapist and the teacher. This is likely to require a short time each day working individually or in small groups with the child. It will be helpful if you can look for ways of practising individual work in classroom activities.

The term 'language impairment' covers a range of difficulties. It is helpful to think of these difficulties in the following ways:

Difficulties in understanding (Receptive language)
- limited knowledge of vocabulary;
- difficulties in understanding meanings of words.

Difficulties in speaking (Expressive language)
- range of uses for which language is employed;
- poor pronounciation;
- disordered structure of language (words omitted, in the wrong order, tense, etc.);
- limited vocabulary;
- stammering.

Different types of difficulty require different treatments. There are many children in our schools who have delayed language development (i.e. language develops normally but at a slower rate) and who benefit from language 'enrichment' activities. This means providing new experiences and teaching the words to use alongside these experiences. Other children have disordered patterns of language development and these pupils require a more intensive approach, using the skills of speech and language therapists and specialised schemes (e.g. the Derbyshire Language Scheme, Makaton sign system, Blissymbols).

If you are working with a child who has a language impairment, it is important that you meet with the speech and language therapist to discuss the child's particular difficulties and how you can provide effective help.

Here are some guidelines for working with language impaired children:

- Get the child's attention before interaction. Often listening and watching are required by the child to help understanding.
- Main content words should be stressed and understanding will be

helped by exaggerated intonation.
• Gesture or use simple signs to help the child understand your message.
• Use short, clear sentences.
• Talk about objects and activities in which the child shows an interest.
• Talk about actions as they are happening.
• Give the child time to respond. Responding in turn is a valuable skill, so try not to dominate the interaction.
• Encourage all spontaneous utterances where appropriate and help the child to feel an equal partner in conversation.
• Do not ask too many questions because they may discourage communication. Balance your talking with comment and description as well.
• Use expansion and extension of the child's utterances.
Expansion - repeat the sentence adding words that were missed out.
Extension - a reply that broadens the focus of attention.
• If sounds or words are said incorrectly by the child, repeat the utterance yourself to show the correct way to say it. This is valuable feedback and should sound natural rather than like a 'correction'.
• Don't try to correct everything at once. Choose a sound, or a concept, to focus on for a week or two.
• No-one enjoys being corrected all the time. We all learn best when we feel relaxed, confident and are enjoying the task. Therefore, praise the child when his/her speech is clear, or new words are attempted, or longer sentences are tried.

Communication impairment

Many pupils with special needs have difficulties communicating effectively as a result of a learning difficulty or physical or sensory impairment. However, there are a small number of pupils whose major problem is an inability to communicate with and make sense of the world around them. These children have normal physical appearance and can hear and see but they fail to understand meanings of language and of social situations. Some of them seem to lack the desire to communicate socially. Children having this kind of difficulty sometimes have a medical diagnosis of autism, or if they are more able, of Asperger's syndrome.

These pupils are relatively rare and most of them are educated in special schools. The more able pupils are in mainstream schools, frequently supported by special needs assistants.

Some of the special characteristics associated with this difficulty are described as follows:

• limited ability to interpret the social cues in any interaction, e.g. the emotions of the listener;
• poor at modifying tone of voice and content of language to 'match' the other half of the conversation;
• limited understanding of jokes and ironic content of language;
• poor play skills or use of imagination;
• stereotyped behaviour or routines.

As a result these pupils need to be taught social and communication skills.

If you are working with a child who has a communication impairment, please remember:

- These children frequently take things literally and this can cause anxiety. It is therefore very important to explain statements and instructions carefully, using words, actions, pictures or role play to help the child's understanding of the situation. Sometimes the child may have unfounded but genuine fears about certain objects, animals or people. You need to be sympathetic if this happens.
- These children need help to know *how* to behave in social situations. Your role might be to show them what is expected and to encourage appropriate behaviour.
- These children tend to withdraw when they cannot make sense of what is going on. You may need to *anticipate* what will cause anxiety and make changes accordingly. It is very helpful if you can prepare the child for what is going to happen next, by talking him or her through the situation, particularly if it is a new experience for the child.
- Physical activity (e.g. jogging, ball play) can be helpful in reducing anxiety and physical tension.
- Do give praise and encouragement. Even though it may not seem to be received, these children need positive feedback and gentle reassurance.

More information about children with communication impairment can be found in: *A Mind of One's Own* - a guide to the special difficulties and needs of the more able person with autism, for parents, professionals and people with autism. (Digby Tantam. The National Autistic Society).

CHAPTER 6

The special needs of special needs assistants

You may be so busy fulfilling your support role with the pupil, the teacher and the school that you may overlook the fact that you yourself have special needs - the need for support, encouragement and for training.

The need for support

The class teacher or co-ordinator with whom you work has a really important influence on whether you feel well supported or not. Those parts of your work affected by this relationship are addressed in Chapter 4 ('The role of the teacher in working with the special needs assistant'). Essentially, you need support to know what you have to do, how you need to do it and how to feel good about it. It is sometimes quite easy to find out the 'what' and 'how' of a task but it is often quite difficult to know whether you have done a good job or not. Accept advice, know your limitations and those of the child, use your initiative to seek alternatives and ask for feedback on what you have done.

You will feel well supported if your school does the following:

• Provides you with a clear job description (see Appendix A).
• Uses your time well:
- i.e. - not 9 - 10 a.m. then 2 - 3 p.m. on the same day.
- not wasted sitting through whole school events when you could be preparing materials.
• Provides a permanent contract:
- too many SNAs are employed on temporary contracts and this is unsatisfactory. There will always be children in mainstream schools who have special needs and need assistance!
• Provides adequate conditions of service:
- even in these enlightened days there are still some assistants who are not allowed in the school staffrooms and some who have to do daily playground duties in their breaktimes.
• Provides career development opportunities:
- through training, you might feel encouraged to do more courses and gain experience in working with different sorts of special need - you might decide to go for additional qualifications. Some SNAs have

been inspired to go on to train as teachers.

- Acts quickly to prevent confusion:

- when problems or misunderstandings arise, it is important that the issues are dealt with speedily and with fairness.

In discussion with groups of assistants, it is clear that a significant number are confused about aspects of their work in schools. Much depends, of course, on the ability of the class teacher to appreciate how best to use special needs assistance. There will be some systems and personalities in schools which are resistant to change, but there will always be *some* changes you can effect. In endeavouring to do this, you will need all those qualities described earlier in this book! ('What makes an effective SNA?'). Constructive criticism, couched in the form of 'improvement suggestions', will often be welcomed.

The following causes of confusion are frequently raised. Some possible solutions are offered:

CAUSES OF CONFUSION	HOW TO PREVENT CONFUSION
1. Lack of background information.	1. Ask questions. Look at school records.
2. No 'named' person to relate to or too many people telling you what to do.	2. Negotiate support from a nominated teacher.
3. Breakdown in communication.	3. Agree arbitrator to resolve difficulties/conflicts.
4. Lack of joint planning.	4. Request time for joint planning.
5. Lack of trust.	5. Encourage trust through consistent supportive work and readiness to work collaboratively.
6. Lack of support.	6. Form a support group with SNAs in your school or in neighbouring schools. Make your 'special needs' known to the special needs co-ordinator.
7. Unclear expectations of staff.	7. Planning, clear job description, clear timetable. Make staff aware of how you are able to work - the special needs co-ordinator can help you with this. Know your limitations.
8. Unclear *how* to work with pupil.	8. Ask the teacher to demonstrate.
9. Unhelpful labelling. e.g. 'Mark's special lady helper'.	9. Negotiate your 'label' (see 'Groundrules', Chapter 2).
10. Assumptions made that the SNA has specialist knowledge.	10. Admit when you don't know, seek information.
11. No 'goals' set for the pupil.	11. Find out, by asking, what are realistic expectations and what objectives or goals should be set.
12. No training.	12. Ask to attend relevant in-service training. Visit other schools to share good practice.

The need for encouragement

From discussion with special needs assistants, it is clear that the job can be fulfilling, creative and rewarding. On the other hand it can be confusing, frustrating and demoralising. Most assistants seem to find themselves somewhere between these two extremes. When asked, the majority of teachers say how much they value the support and skills which SNAs offer, but there is one problem - they don't tell the SNAs that! Only a few schools provide constructive feedback on a regular basis to their assistants. This lack of encouragement from school staff is not deliberate but often happens. This is because, on the one hand, there is no space for evaluation of SNA input and also because teachers themselves do not receive enough positive feedback. (You can support the teacher by providing some of this!)

One of the most consistent messages coming from special needs assistants who have had no training is that they lack confidence in what they do. This can be very inhibiting and prevents participation and creativity. It is a particular problem for SNAs who are newly appointed and who are unsure of their role. The need for creating regular opportunities to review progress and provide encouragement is clear if confidence is to be boosted.

Teachers now have annual reviews or appraisal of their work. This sort of process could also be used for SNAs, allowing time for celebration of success and encouraging future projects.

The need for training

Why do we need training?

SNAs vary greatly in their background experience. A number are trained teachers who do not want the responsibility of a full class and full time working. Some have no formal qualifications at all. Recent research by the National Foundation for Educational Research (NFER, Fletcher-Campbell) has shown that assistants range from ex-dinner ladies or parent volunteers who want more involvement with classroom life to people considering a career in teaching and who are exploring this by way of working as an assistant. Others are qualified teachers who wish to return to teaching following a career break and who see an assistant's role as a way of getting back into schools. All SNAs have experience of working with children either in school e.g. as 'dinner ladies', through voluntary agencies e.g. brownies, and the majority bring parenting skills to their role. This wide variation in background experience shows a clear need for training, especially since the role has become more educational with assistants being much more involved in the child's learning. The following scenario highlights this need:

> An assistant described a discussion between the class teacher, the parents of a child with special needs and herself. She was asked by the parents what particular training she had had in order for her to support their child and she had to say that she had no special training and had to rely on the guidance of the class teacher.

Parents need to know that their children are supported by people who know what they are doing. Schools need to be sure that children who need assistance are given informed and confident support from fully trained assistants.

Whatever their background experience, most assistants start the job with no specific training either about the role or about the special needs they might meet. Most assistants are given no formalised in-service training once they have started the job. Most learn by 'trial and error' on a day to day basis and by watching teachers at work. This is far from ideal and can lead to confusion and feelings of being undervalued, particularly in secondary schools where assistants have several different teachers to work with.

Certainly as an assistant you can learn a great deal by watching good teachers at work. There are tried and tested ways of handling children which you can successfully copy. This works best if you ask for a particular skill to be demonstrated and talked through with you before and after the activity so that you are clear about how and why a particular approach works.

There should be one teacher in the school, either a class teacher or special needs co-ordinator, who carries the main responsibility for your day to day work. This responsibility should include 'on the job' training, with opportunities provided for planning and evaluation of what you do. Start by identifying together what you need to know and planning a programme to meet your needs. Ideally your staff supporter should be able to watch you at work in order to provide helpful suggestions. Of course, this can only work well when the teacher responsible is given time to do this - many school managers are now becoming aware of this need and are providing some space in the week to allow this to happen.

What should the training involve?

There are two aspects of SNA training:

- Training to understand the roles and responsibilities of working as an assistant (see Chapter 2).
- Training in specific skills needed to meet the special needs of the pupils (see Chapter 5).

Who should be involved?

Training for SNAs is, in one sense, an ongoing process which takes place in the school on a 'drip-feed' basis as the teacher and SNA work together on a daily basis to determine ground rules, to plan programmes and to clarify responsibilities. The school has the responsibility for this aspect of training and as an assistant you have a responsibility to the child to ask when you are unclear about what is expected, e.g. you may be asked to work with a child using a computer and you may not know how to do this. Immediate training will be necessary.

Margaret Balshaw, in her book *Help in the Classroom,* gives useful advice and provides workshop materials for schools to use in school based in-service training. These materials enable schools to make better use of classroom assistants. She suggests six principles of good practice for schools. These six principles are:

1. Classroom assistants should be clear about their roles and responsibilities.
2. Classroom assistants should understand the communication systems in the school.
3. Classroom assistants should be seen positively as part of the provision to meet children's needs.
4. Classroom assistants should be part of a working team.
5. Classroom assistants should be encouraged to make use of their personal skills.
6. Classroom assistants should be helped to develop their personal and professional needs alongside other members of staff.

Activities and scenarios are provided which encourage schools to look at each of these six principles in order to encourage partnership working and to plan more efficient and effective ways of using assistance.

Training in specific skills

There is clearly a need for specific training e.g. if you are working with a pupil who has cerebral palsy you may need to learn certain physiotherapy routines, or if you work with a child who has a language impairment you will need to know what particular programme is relevant and why. In these cases the physiotherapist and speech therapist will be the people who can train you (and the teacher) to use the right approaches. SNAs frequently ask for training in managing behaviour. The educational psychologist can give support in recommending ways of working with pupils who have emotional or behavioural difficulties.

Most LEAs have teams of advisory teachers who support children with special needs (e.g. visual impairment, hearing impairment, physical disability) and these teachers are able to support you with background information and practical advice.

How should the training be delivered?

Training is ideally delivered within the schools, through teachers and assistants working together with input from other professionals on a programme to deliver training in both roles and responsibilities and in specific skills.

This is not usually possible because schools may have other priorities for in-service training and also small schools may not have the money, space or time to provide such training. High quality training needs a considerable amount of *time* which not all schools can offer.

In Hampshire we have put together an annual training course based on needs identified by schools and SNAs. There are six modules (each a full day) delivered over a six month period, and a seventh module which is a school based project. The course leads to a City and Guilds qualification - the Certificate in Learning Support (732-1).

The topics covered are as follows:

Roles and responsibilities
Emotional and behavioural difficulties
Learning difficulties (including specific learning difficulties)
Hearing impairment
Visual impairment
Physical disability
Language difficulties
School team approaches (teachers also attend)

The course is designed and delivered by local authority educational psychologists and special educational needs advisory and support staff.

School staff are much involved in the course and have to provide a mentor for the assistant and an internal assessor. The SNA keeps a learning log to show evidence of competencies considered necessary in the role.

Following each module the assistants are encouraged to share what they have learned with the teachers they work with. During the course a course tutor (advisory teacher or educational psychologist) visits the school to discuss the school based project and to encourage partnership working. The final session involves the class teachers and SNAs in workshop activities to promote effective partnership working. It is clear that much benefit is gained when teachers and assistants work together for the good of the children in their care and it would be desirable for both teachers and SNAs to attend all the course together but this is not always realistic financially. However, this may be an option in the future.

The good news for assistants is that many education authorities are now recognising the need for high quality training and are investigating ways that this can be provided.

Some final comments

The job of a classroom assistant has changed significantly over the last ten years. The negative concept of a 'non teaching assistant' employed to 'mix glazes, back books, clean paintpots and clear up messes' (to quote from a real job description of 1983) has gradually become obsolete - although there are still pockets of ignorance in our schools!

This idea of an assistant as a general dogsbody was replaced by the notion of an assistant as 'an extra pair of hands' a seemingly more positive concept but one which by implication suggests a 'reactive automaton' - not recognising that there is a thinking brain making the hands work!

In the last five years, however, the potential of assistants who are, in the main, employed to support children with special needs has been increasingly recognised. Schools are beginning to address the issues of support and training and the result is a more effective use of assistance and a much healthier concept of the role.

The happiest assistants are those who are valued by their colleagues in school and who are clear about their roles and responsibilities. In this handbook I have tried to suggest ways of working together in schools which will lead to a greater understanding of the role of a special needs assistant. I hope that it will encourage teachers and assistants to look together at how best to support each other and how best to support the pupils with whom they work. Some schools are well on the way to success - others, like Thursday's child, have 'far to go'!

Headteachers who employ assistants have a direct influence on and responsibility for the quality of experience of the assistant in school. I hope this book encourages school managers to think carefully and creatively about how they manage this resource and about the need for clear policy and procedures.

Above all, I hope I have given practical advice and reassurance to classroom assistants which will enable them to be clearer about their roles and responsibilities and help them to work more confidently in supporting children, teachers and schools.

Appendix A

A Job Description Suggestion for a Special Needs Assistant

This job description is for an SNA working in a mainstream school. Specific adaptations would be necessary for assistants working in special schools.

JOB TITLE: SPECIAL NEEDS ASSISTANT
POST HOLDER:
GRADE:
RESPONSIBLE TO: Headteacher/Class Teacher/Special Needs Co-ordinator
RECEIVES INSTRUCTION FROM: Headteacher/Class Teacher/Special Needs Co-ordinator
PURPOSE OF JOB:

To assist in the support and integration of children with special educational needs within a mainstream school.

JOB DUTIES:

A. *Supporting the Pupil*

1. Drawing on knowledge of various forms of special needs, to develop an understanding of the specific needs of the child/ren concerned.
2. Taking into account the special needs involved, to aid the child/ren to learn as effectively as possible both in group situations and on his/her own by, for example:
- clarifying and explaining instructions;
- ensuring child is able to use equipment and materials provided;
- motivating and encouraging child as required;
- assisting in weak areas e.g. language, behaviour, reading, spelling, handwriting/presentation etc;
- helping pupils to concentrate on and finish work set;
- meeting physical needs as required whilst encouraging independence;
- liaising with class teacher devising complementary learning activities.
3. To establish a supportive relationship with the child/ren concerned.
4. To encourage acceptance and integration of the child with special needs.
5. To develop methods of promoting/reinforcing children's self-esteem.

B. *Supporting the Teacher*

1. To assist, with class teacher (and other professionals as appropriate), in the development of a suitable programme of support for child/ren with special needs.
2. In conjunction with the class teacher and/or other professionals to develop a system of recording child's progress.
3. To contribute to the maintenance of child/ren's progress records.

4. To participate in the evaluation of the support programme.
5. To provide regular feedback about the child to the teacher.

C. *Supporting the School*

1. Where appropriate, to develop a relationship to foster links between home and school.
2. To liaise, advise and consult with other members of the team supporting the child/ren when asked to do so.
3. To contribute to reviews of the pupil's progress.
4. To attend relevant in-service training.
5. To be aware of school procedures.

Any other tasks as directed by Head Teacher which fall within the purview of the post.

Appendix B

The roles of supporting professionals

During the course of your work in school, it is likely that you will come across one or more of the following professionals:

Physiotherapists

The physiotherapist identifies a child's main physical problems and devises a programme of treatment to overcome them. This may include: exercises, the use of splints or other aids, and advice on seating and general classroom handling.

Speech and Language Therapists

Speech and language therapists work with children who may have a wide range of disorders affecting their understanding and use of speech and/or language. They will assess the child's progress and provide a programme of activities aimed at developing: listening skills, use of speech sounds, development of sentence structure etc.

Educational Psychologists

Educational psychologists visit all schools on a regular basis in order to support children and the adults who work with them. They are called on to help and advise on a variety of educational problems. They may also devise programmes and carry out individual assessments. In addition, they are heavily involved in assessment carried out under the 1981 Education Act, which may lead to a statement of special educational needs.

Teacher Advisers

As the title suggests, teacher advisers give advice to class teachers on specific issues. In addition, they may teach or assess individual children. Each teacher is usually a specialist in a specific area e.g. learning difficulties, hearing impairment, physical disability, visual impairment etc.

School Medical Officers (Clinical Medical Officers [CMO])

School medical officers are doctors who visit schools on a regular basis in order to see all children at certain stages in their school lives, and particular children as the need arises. They are able to provide diagnosis and to give advice about the medical implications of certain conditions.

References

Ainscow, M. and Tweddle, D. A. (1988), *Encouraging Classroom Success*. London: David Fulton.
Audit Commission/HMI (1992), *Getting in on the Act. A Management Handbook for schools and LEA's*. London: HMSO.
Audit Commission/HMI (1992), *Getting the Act Together.* London: HMSO.
Balshaw, M.H. (1991), *Help in the Classroom*. London: David Fulton.
Bennett, A. (1985), *Meeting the Integration Needs of Partially Hearing Unit Pupils* A.E.P. Journal, Vol.6 No.5. - Supplement.
Blind and Partially Sighted Children in Britain, The R.N.I.B. Survey, Vol.12 London: HMSO.
Fletcher-Campbell, F. (1992), *'How Can We Use an Extra Pair of Hands?'*, *British Journal of Special Education*, Vol.19, No.4.
Formal Assessment Procedures: Guidance for Parents, Hampshire Education Authority.
Maines, B. and Robinson, G., *You Can - You Know You Can;* Course handbook to accompany workshops on the self-concept approach. Bristol : Lame Duck Publishing.
Fenton, M. (1992), *Working Together Towards Independence.* London: RADAR - the Royal Association for Disability and Rehabilitation.
Mallon, B.(1987), *An Introduction to Counselling Skills for Special Educational Needs.* Manchester University Press.
Meeting Special Needs Within the National Curriculum (1989), Hampshire Education Authority.
Principles of Good Practice - A Tool for Self-evaluation (1992), Guidelines produced by the Hampshire Inspection and Advisory Support Service, Hampshire Education Authority.
Special Educational Needs (1978) Report of the Committee of Handicapped Children and Young People, HMSO (The Warnock Report).
The Education Act (1981). London: HMSO.
The Children Act (1989). London: HMSO.